Table of Contents

Algebra 2: A Teaching Textbook™
2.0 Version
Answer Key and Test Bank
Greg Sabouri and Shawn Sabouri

Printed in the United States of America.

ISBN: 978-0-9835812-5-3

Teaching Textbooks, Inc.
P. O. Box 16310
Oklahoma City, OK 73113
www.teachingtextbooks.com

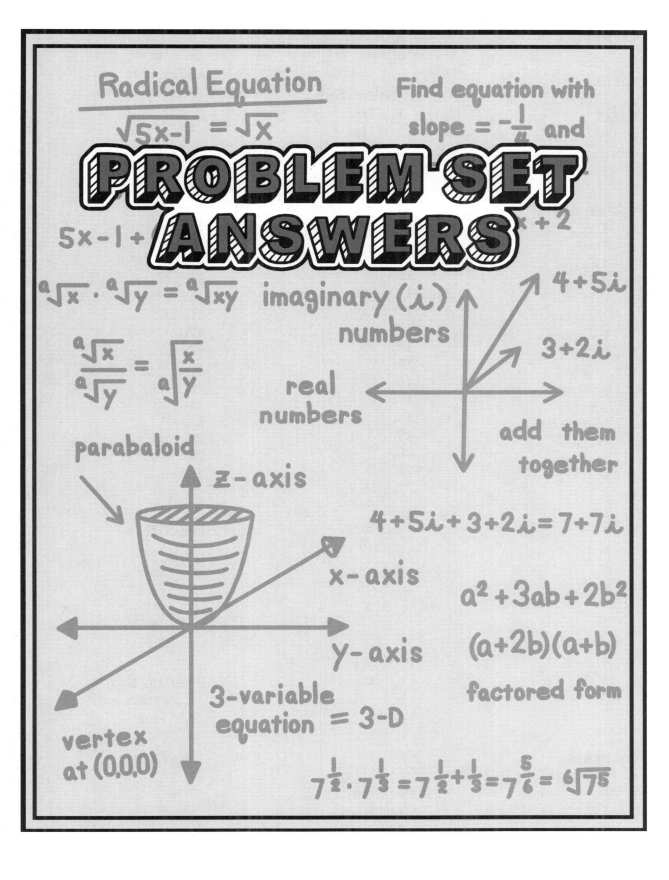

Radical Equation

$$\sqrt{5x-1} = \sqrt{x}$$

PROBLEM SET ANSWERS

Find equation with slope $= -\frac{1}{u}$ and

$5x-1+$

$x+2$

$$\sqrt[a]{x} \cdot \sqrt[a]{y} = \sqrt[a]{xy}$$

imaginary (i) numbers

$4+5i$

$3+2i$

$$\frac{\sqrt[a]{x}}{\sqrt[a]{y}} = \sqrt[a]{\frac{x}{y}}$$

real numbers

add them together

parabaloid

z-axis

$$4+5i + 3+2i = 7+7i$$

x-axis

$$a^2 + 3ab + 2b^2$$

y-axis

$(a+2b)(a+b)$

factored form

3-variable equation $= 3$-D

vertex at $(0,0,0)$

$$7^{\frac{1}{2}} \cdot 7^{\frac{1}{3}} = 7^{\frac{1}{2}+\frac{1}{3}} = 7^{\frac{5}{6}} = \sqrt[6]{7^5}$$

CHAPTER 1

Practice 1
a. Expression
b. C
c. E
d. B
e. 3

Problem Set 1
1. True
2. False
3. True
4. C
5. B
6. A
7. E
8. C
9. Algebra
10. Arithmetic
11. Algebra
12. Expression
13. Equation
14. Expression
15. E
16. A
17. D
18. C
19. C
20. B
21. A
22. D
23. $\dfrac{7}{3}$
24. 8
25. $\dfrac{2}{3}$

Practice 2
a. B
b. D
c. E

d. C
e. 8

Problem Set 2
1. True
2. True
3. False
4. False
5. A
6. E
7. C
8. C
9. E
10. 18
11. 26
12. 13
13. 3
14. 16
15. 7
16. D
17. E
18. A
19. A
20. B
21. D
22. D
23. $\dfrac{7}{5}$
24. $\dfrac{10}{3}$
25. $\dfrac{6}{5}$

Practice 3
a. A
b. 5
c. 5
d. 7
e. 3

Problem Set 3
1. True
2. True

3. True
4. A
5. E
6. 0
7. 8
8. 36
9. $\dfrac{7}{8}$
10. $\dfrac{14}{3}$
11. C
12. B
13. E
14. C
15. D
16. C
17. C
18. 2
19. 9
20. 24
21. 12
22. 3
23. 8
24. 11
25. 5.5

Practice 4
a. 6
b. 4
c. 7
d. $\dfrac{119}{5}$
e. 8%

Problem Set 4
1. False
2. True
3. 7
4. 3
5. 1
6. 72
7. $\dfrac{9}{5}$

8. D
9. B
10. A
11. B
12. A
13. E
14. 10
15. 5
16. 10
17. 16
18. 5
19. 10
20. 9
21. 5
22. $\dfrac{59}{2}$
23. 7.5%

Practice 5
a. −10
b. 21
c. 2
d. 1
e. $2

Problem Set 5
1. False
2. True
3. False
4. D
5. E
6. E
7. −5,500
8. −48
9. −8
10. −6
11. −24
12. −24
13. −36
14. 36
15. 2
16. C
17. A

18. 17
19. 6
20. 6
21. 5
22. 8
23. $\dfrac{22}{5}$
24. 3
25. $4

Practice 6
a. $-\dfrac{5}{8}$
b. Yes
c. −29
d. −21
e. 60

Problem Set 6
1. False
2. True
3. True
4. −4.7
5. $\dfrac{5}{12}$
6. −14
7. 48
8. $-\dfrac{4}{7}$
9. −3
10. −5
11. 9
12. Yes
13. No
14. No
15. C
16. E
17. 8
18. 5
19. 43
20. 15
21. 3
22. 18

23. 27
24. −6

CHAPTER 2

Practice 7
a. No
b. Yes
c. Yes
d. −15
e. $1.75

Problem Set 7
1. True
2. True
3. A
4. B
5. C
6. D
7. −16
8. −181
9. −16.5
10. 5
11. $-\dfrac{1}{4}$
12. −220
13. No
14. Yes
15. Yes
16. Yes
17. −40
18. 1
19. 70
20. 27
21. −28
22. 108
23. −16
24. $2.75

Practice 8
a. Yes
b. Yes
c. No
d. 2
e. −5

Problem Set 8
1. True
2. True
3. 17.5
4. 0
5. 118.75
6. 6
7. $\dfrac{3}{10}$
8. B
9. D
10. Yes
11. No
12. Yes
13. Yes
14. Yes
15. 2
16. 60
17. 1
18. −91
19. $-\dfrac{1}{9}$
20. −63.2
21. 63
22. 11
23. $-\dfrac{21}{4}$
24. $1.75

Practice 9
a. Yes
b. Yes
c. 14
d. 15
e. 5,000 dresses

Problem Set 9
1. True
2. True
3. True
4. −9
5. −1
6. 0
7. −9
8. 1
9. 16.8
10. Yes
11. Yes
12. Yes
13. No
14. Yes
15. 9
16. 1
17. 9
18. 4
19. −4
20. 49.5
21. 5
22. 1
23. 5
24. 100,000 boxes

Practice 10
a. Yes
b. $\dfrac{5}{6}$
c. −24
d. 9
e. $50

Problem Set 10
1. True
2. False
3. −9
4. $-\dfrac{1}{15}$
5. −36.8
6. −7
7. 1
8. 11
9. Yes
10. No
11. Yes
12. D
13. A
14. C

15. 3
16. 42
17. -27
18. 21
19. 7
20. -14
21. 5
22. 1
23. $45

Practice 11
a. 15
b. Yes
c. D
d. -20
e. $80,000

Problem Set 11
1. True
2. True
3. -8
4. 16
5. 8
6. -25
7. 2
8. 16
9. Yes
10. No
11. Yes
12. E
13. C
14. B
15. 7
16. 2
17. -320
18. $\dfrac{5}{3}$
19. 26
20. -5
21. 15
22. -1
23. $300,000

Practice 12
a. E
b. Yes
c. E
d. 3
e. 32 patients

Problem Set 12
1. True
2. False
3. True
4. -30
5. 9
6. 3
7. 62
8. 18
9. B
10. C
11. No
12. No
13. Yes
14. E
15. B
16. C
17. 3
18. 2
19. $-\dfrac{5}{2}$
20. -45
21. -135
22. $-\dfrac{1}{2}$
23. 5
24. 360 customers

Practice 13
a. Yes
b. No
c. -8
d. $\dfrac{5}{13}$
e. $24

Problem Set 13
1. True
2. True
3. $-\dfrac{7}{6}$
4. -10
5. 0
6. -16
7. B
8. D
9. Yes
10. No
11. No
12. A
13. E
14. D
15. B
16. -20
17. -6
18. -46
19. 4
20. $\dfrac{3}{7}$
21. 20
22. -1
23. $20

Practice 14
a. E
b. 1
c. False equation
d. Identity
e. $7,500

Problem Set 14
1. False
2. True
3. True
4. -32
5. 6
6. 0
7. -57
8. C

9. E
10. Yes
11. Yes
12. A
13. B
14. E
15. B
16. -3
17. $-\dfrac{6}{5}$
18. -5
19. 42
20. False equation
21. Identity
22. $15,000

17. $-\dfrac{23}{2}$
18. 3
19. -6
20. -2
21. -6
22. -4
23. 2 hours

Practice 15
a. D
b. A
c. 5
d. $-\dfrac{5}{6}$
e. $\dfrac{1}{2}$ hour

Problem Set 15
1. True
2. False
3. 19
4. -13.5
5. -3
6. 11
7. 4
8. B
9. A
10. Yes
11. Yes
12. D
13. C
14. E
15. E
16. B

CHAPTER 3

Practice 16
a. C
b. No
c. C
d. 3
e. 3 seconds

Problem Set 16
1. False
2. True
3. True
4. False
5. -15
6. 27
7. 4
8. -9
9. E
10. C
11. Yes
12. No
13. A
14. C
15. E
16. B
17. B
18. A
19. $\dfrac{5}{8}$
20. 2
21. -3
22. 6
23. 2
24. 3 seconds

Practice 17
a. Yes
b. B
c. C
d. -11
e. 8 seconds

Problem Set 17
1. True
2. True
3. -2
4. $-\dfrac{3}{10}$
5. -1
6. -2
7. -14
8. No
9. No
10. Yes
11. D
12. D
13. B
14. A
15. D
16. A
17. -30
18. 2
19. $\dfrac{6}{5}$
20. -8
21. Identity
22. $\dfrac{3}{2}$
23. 140 seconds

Practice 18
a. Yes
b. B
c. A
d. $\dfrac{4}{5}$
e. 7.5 pounds

Problem Set 18
1. True
2. True
3. False
4. -16
5. 39
6. -3

7. 0
8. 0
9. Yes
10. Yes
11. No
12. C
13. D
14. A
15. E
16. E
17. B
18. $\dfrac{5}{9}$
19. 2
20. 33
21. $-\dfrac{24}{5}$
22. 1
23. 15 pounds

Practice 19
a. No
b. E
c. A
d. -4
e. 4 milliliters

Problem Set 19
1. True
2. True
3. 12
4. -5
5. -30
6. 4
7. -10
8. No
9. Yes
10. A
11. B
12. D
13. C
14. A
15. B

16. 9
17. $-\dfrac{1}{7}$
18. $\dfrac{1}{12}$
19. -28
20. False equation
21. -3
22. 30 milligrams

Practice 20
a. No
b. D
c. A
d. $\dfrac{7}{4}$
e. 2 hours

Problem Set 20
1. True
2. False
3. 4
4. -24.6
5. 49
6. 4
7. -3
8. Yes
9. No
10. B
11. C
12. B
13. E
14. D
15. D
16. $-\dfrac{12}{5}$
17. 1
18. $\dfrac{3}{14}$
19. $-\dfrac{1}{2}$
20. -6

21. $\dfrac{11}{3}$
22. 1 hour

Practice 21
a. Yes
b. D
c. $\dfrac{5}{7}$
d. $\dfrac{1}{10}$
e. 5.7 gallons

Problem Set 21
1. True
2. False
3. -7
4. 21
5. 7
6. -20
7. 3
8. Yes
9. Yes
10. D
11. A
12. D
13. E
14. A
15. E
16. $\dfrac{5}{8}$
17. $\dfrac{5}{3}$
18. $\dfrac{29}{7}$
19. -1
20. $\dfrac{3}{14}$
21. $\dfrac{1}{3}$
22. 75 cartons

CHAPTER 4

Practice 22
a. 2.89
b. Yes
c. E
d. D
e. 5 balcony tickets

Problem Set 22
1. True
2. False
3. False
4. 2
5. 64
6. 3
7. 12.25
8. -50
9. No
10. Yes
11. D
12. B
13. B
14. C
15. A
16. B
17. D
18. -25
19. 5
20. $\dfrac{4}{3}$
21. -2
22. -16
23. 6 packages

Practice 23
a. 9
b. C
c. E
d. 17
e. 33

Problem Set 23
1. True
2. True
3. 64
4. $\dfrac{1}{125}$
5. 9
6. -4
7. -10
8. No
9. Yes
10. B
11. E
12. A
13. D
14. D
15. C
16. C
17. -5
18. 9
19. 0
20. -3
21. 7
22. 86

Practice 24
a. -48
b. B
c. E
d. $-\dfrac{8}{3}$
e. 1.6 hours

Problem Set 24
1. True
2. True
3. False
4. 256
5. -17
6. 2^5 or 32
7. -50
8. $-\dfrac{1}{27}$

9. Yes
10. No
11. E
12. C
13. A
14. E
15. B
16. B
17. 12
18. $\dfrac{3}{2}$
19. 1
20. $\dfrac{14}{3}$
21. 1 hour

Practice 25
a. Yes
b. C
c. A
d. E
e. $30,000,000

Problem Set 25
1. False
2. True
3. $\dfrac{1}{25}$
4. -1
5. -4
6. 10
7. 74.088
8. No
9. Yes
10. A
11. D
12. C
13. A
14. E
15. B
16. D
17. B
18. -4

19. 27
20. $-\dfrac{4}{5}$
21. $\dfrac{9}{4}$
22. $2,000

Practice 26
a. -16
b. B
c. E
d. C
e. 2.5 ounces

Problem Set 26
1. True
2. True
3. -81
4. 6
5. 1
6. -6
7. -8
8. Yes
9. No
10. C
11. D
12. B
13. E
14. D
15. A
16. C
17. B
18. -6
19. 7
20. $\dfrac{10}{3}$
21. $\dfrac{20}{3}$
22. 6 ounces

Practice 27
a. Yes
b. Yes
c. D
d. D
e. 2 hours

Problem Set 27
1. False
2. True
3. 38
4. 1
5. 0
6. -36
7. -27
8. Yes
9. Yes
10. B
11. D
12. A
13. E
14. C
15. A
16. 0
17. 10
18. -4
19. $\dfrac{2}{5}$
20. $\dfrac{6}{5}$
21. 1 hour

Practice 28
a. No
b. B
c. E
d. D
e. 12 gallons

Problem Set 28
1. True
2. False
3. 10^7 or 10,000,000

4. 10
5. 6^2 or 36
6. 19
7. -10
8. Yes
9. No
10. C
11. E
12. A
13. D
14. D
15. A
16. 2
17. -11
18. $-\dfrac{7}{2}$
19. $\dfrac{13}{3}$
20. -2
21. 40 gallons

Practice 29
a. 3.4×10^{-9}
b. 6.3×10^{12}
c. 2.05×10^{-4}
d. C
e. 12 dimes

Problem Set 29
1. True
2. False
3. False
4. 2.3×10^8
5. 1.7×10^{-9}
6. 9.5×10^{12}
7. 1.305×10^{29}
8. 2×10^{-14}
9. 2.86×10^{-4}
10. No
11. Yes
12. D
13. E

14. A
15. C
16. D
17. B
18. -14
19. -7
20. -2
21. $\dfrac{8}{9}$
22. 32 nickels

CHAPTER 5

Practice 30
a. 258,000,000,000
b. 4
c. D
d. A
e. 6 years old

Problem Set 30
1. True
2. False
3. 895,000,000,000
4. 0.0000000506
5. 6
6. 2.73×10^{27}
7. 9
8. 3
9. 0
10. D
11. C
12. D
13. Yes
14. Yes
15. 6
16. $\dfrac{1}{4}$
17. B
18. E
19. A
20. Identity
21. $\dfrac{2}{15}$
22. 5
23. 12 years old

Practice 31
a. 1.56×10^{-12}
b. Rational
c. Irrational
d. 2.24
e. $350

Problem Set 31
1. True
2. True
3. True
4. 2.38×10^{12}
5. 9.2×10^{-10}
6. 1.5×10^{-5}
7. -4
8. 4
9. 2.68×10^{-12}
10. Rational
11. Irrational
12. 2.65
13. 3.32
14. Yes
15. No
16. C
17. A
18. B
19. 3
20. 1
21. $-\dfrac{8}{3}$
22. $15

Practice 32
a. $\sqrt{2}$
b. $\sqrt[3]{35}$
c. Rational
d. C
e. 40 nickels

Problem Set 32
1. True
2. True
3. 2.39
4. 0.0000075
5. $\sqrt{35}$
6. 1.176×10^{19}
7. $\sqrt{5}$
8. 2
9. $\sqrt[3]{36}$
10. A
11. C
12. A
13. Rational
14. Irrational
15. No
16. Yes
17. E
18. D
19. B
20. 31
21. $-\dfrac{9}{5}$
22. $\dfrac{3}{2}$
23. 38 dimes

Practice 33
a. $\sqrt[3]{5}$
b. D
c. E
d. C
e. $8,000

Problem Set 33
1. False
2. False
3. 0.000042
4. 1,835,000
5. 2.59×10^{8}
6. 6.53×10^{-10}
7. $\sqrt{22}$
8. $\sqrt[3]{4}$
9. $\sqrt[3]{45}$
10. B
11. A
12. E
13. Irrational
14. Rational
15. Yes
16. No

17. E
18. B
19. A
20. D
21. 1
22. 4
23. 12
24. $15,000

Practice 34
a. E
b. A
c. E
d. B
e. 90

Problem Set 34
1. True
2. False
3. 2.35×10^{-6}
4. 9.9×10^{12}
5. 3.87
6. 4.58
7. $\sqrt{57}$
8. $\sqrt[3]{3}$
9. C
10. D
11. B
12. A
13. D
14. E
15. D
16. A
17. C
18. B
19. E
20. $\dfrac{4}{23}$
21. 2
22. 6
23. 40

Practice 35
a. D
b. B
c. B
d. E
e. 4 hours

Problem Set 35
1. True
2. True
3. 3.68×10^{23}
4. 2.52×10^{-2}
5. 8×10^{5}
6. D
7. A
8. C
9. B
10. C
11. A
12. Yes
13. No
14. D
15. C
16. E
17. B
18. C
19. 2
20. 1
21. 4
22. 2 hours

Practice 36
a. D
b. E
c. E
d. A
e. 12 years old

Problem Set 36
1. True
2. True
3. 88,100,000
4. 0.000035

5. C
6. E
7. A
8. C
9. D
10. D
11. B
12. E
13. A
14. C
15. Yes
16. Yes
17. B
18. D
19. E
20. B
21. -2
22. $\dfrac{13}{5}$
23. $\dfrac{13}{7}$
24. 10 years old

Practice 37
a. $4^{\frac{5}{3}}$
b. 4
c. $6^{\frac{5}{6}}$
d. $5^{\frac{1}{4}}$
e. 57

Problem Set 37
1. True
2. True
3. $8^{\frac{1}{2}}$
4. $12^{\frac{1}{4}}$
5. $2^{\frac{4}{3}}$
6. $\sqrt{105}$
7. 3
8. B

9. C
10. D
11. $5^{\frac{5}{6}}$
12. $7^{\frac{1}{4}}$
13. D
14. E
15. E
16. B
17. D
18. A
19. D
20. $\dfrac{7}{3}$
21. 3
22. $-\dfrac{3}{5}$
23. 73

CHAPTER 6

Practice 38
a. E
b. $4^{\frac{7}{15}}$
c. D
d. C
e. 200 gallons

Problem Set 38
1. True
2. True
3. True
4. 9.25×10^{17}
5. 3.37×10^{-13}
6. $\sqrt{6}$
7. E
8. A
9. D
10. $11^{\frac{7}{12}}$
11. $5^{\frac{7}{15}}$
12. B
13. E
14. C
15. A
16. A
17. -7
18. $5, -5$
19. $\dfrac{10}{3}$
20. $9, -9$
21. $\dfrac{4}{5}$
22. D
23. 3.75 pounds

Practice 39
a. -5.83
b. D
c. E
d. B
e. 6 in., 18 in.

Problem Set 39
1. True
2. True
3. 3.24
4. -5.16
5. B
6. E
7. A
8. C
9. $3^{\frac{9}{10}}$
10. $6^{\frac{5}{4}}$
11. No
12. Yes
13. A
14. D
15. A
16. $+3, -3$
17. -1
18. $-\dfrac{4}{3}$
19. A
20. C
21. D
22. 24 ft., 3 ft.

Practice 40
a. B
b. 5
c. 0, 7
d. $-3, -4$
e. 2 ft.

Problem Set 40
1. True
2. True
3. 1.155×10^{-6}
4. 9×10^{-8}
5. $\sqrt[3]{36}$
6. $8^{\frac{5}{6}}$
7. $\sqrt{10}$
8. D
9. $2^{\frac{13}{6}}$
10. E
11. C
12. A
13. D
14. B
15. D
16. 8
17. B
18. C
19. 0, 4
20. 0, 3
21. $-2, -4$
22. 3 ft.

Practice 41
a. D
b. A
c. $-\dfrac{1}{3}, -5$
d. $\dfrac{1}{5}, -2$
e. 9 ft., 15 ft.

Problem Set 41
1. False
2. False
3. -1.26
4. -18.24
5. $\sqrt[5]{4}$
6. E
7. C
8. $5^{\frac{13}{12}}$
9. D
10. B
11. E
12. E
13. B

14. A
15. 5, −5
16. 3
17. 1, −7
18. $0, -\dfrac{1}{2}$
19. $-\dfrac{1}{2}, -3$
20. $\dfrac{1}{3}, -2$
21. 6 ft., 10 ft.

Practice 42
a. A
b. E
c. C
d. B
e. 13 ft.

Problem Set 42
1. True
2. True
3. 7.92×10^{18}
4. 1.05×10^{-11}
5. $2^{\frac{3}{5}}$
6. $\sqrt[6]{3}$
7. D
8. C
9. D
10. D
11. Yes
12. Yes
13. C
14. B
15. E
16. $\dfrac{20}{3}$
17. 0, 2
18. B
19. E
20. A
21. 7 ft.

Practice 43
a. 0.46
b. E
c. D
d. A
e. 7, 21

Problem Set 43
1. True
2. True
3. 2.52
4. −0.02
5. D
6. $8^{\frac{13}{20}}$
7. $5^{\frac{1}{3}}$
8. E
9. C
10. C
11. E
12. A
13. D
14. A
15. −3
16. $0, \dfrac{1}{3}$
17. 10, 1
18. D
19. A
20. C
21. 5, 10

CHAPTER 7

Practice 44

a. $a = -3$, $b = -5$, $c = -1$
b. B
c. 9
d. $-\dfrac{3}{2}, -4$
e. 76 women

Problem Set 44

1. True
2. True
3. $a = 3$, $b = 7$, $c = 2$
4. $a = -2$, $b = -9$, $c = -4$
5. 3
6. C
7. E
8. D
9. B
10. E
11. C
12. A
13. A
14. 4
15. $-\dfrac{9}{4}$
16. 64
17. $5, -5$
18. $0, 2$
19. $4, 3$
20. $-\dfrac{5}{3}, -3$
21. 154 guests

Practice 45

a. A
b. 11
c. 48
d. C
e. 182 quarters

Problem Set 45

1. $a = -4$, $b = 7$, $c = -9$
2. $a = 3$, $b = -1$, $c = -1$
3. 402,500,000
4. 0.00003009
5. E
6. C
7. $\sqrt[4]{55}$
8. Yes
9. No
10. A
11. B
12. D
13. D
14. 7
15. -7
16. 50
17. 5
18. $0, \dfrac{1}{2}$
19. $-1, -7$
20. E
21. 16 nickels

Practice 46

a. E
b. 4 (-1 is extraneous)
c. 4, 5
d. $-\dfrac{1}{7}$
e. 16 years old

Problem Set 46

1. True
2. False
3. 7.54×10^{-8}
4. 2.35×10^{15}
5. B
6. $3^{\frac{26}{15}}$

7. $7^{\frac{1}{6}}$
8. C
9. B
10. D
11. B
12. E
13. A
14. 5 (2 is extraneous)
15. $-2, -3$
16. 2
17. $0, -2$
18. 11
19. 9
20. $-\dfrac{4}{9}$
21. 11 years old

Practice 47

a. D
b. 18
c. $\dfrac{13}{4}$
d. $-8, 5$
e. $20,000

Problem Set 47

1. -2.00
2. 6.72
3. A
4. $5^{\frac{5}{14}}$
5. B
6. D
7. E
8. E
9. No
10. Yes
11. A
12. A
13. E
14. 12
15. -1

16. $\dfrac{29}{2}$
17. 5
18. $0, -8$
19. $-9, 7$
20. $30,000

Practice 48
 a. E
 b. 6 (-1 is extraneous)
 c. 2
 d. C
 e. 12 hours

Problem Set 48
 1. $a = 2$, $b = 3$, $c = -1$
 2. $a = 1$, $b = -4$, $c = 5$
 3. 20,600,000
 4. 0.000071
 5. D
 6. $6^{\frac{11}{12}}$
 7. $11^{\frac{7}{4}}$
 8. E
 9. A
10. D
11. B
12. D
13. A
14. 7
15. 21
16. 5 (-2 is extraneous)
17. 3
18. $-\dfrac{5}{3}$
19. D
20. 60 seconds

CHAPTER 8

Practice 49
a. E
b. C
c. A
d. B
e. 30 degrees

Problem Set 49
1. True
2. False
3. 4.55
4. 1.51
5. D
6. E
7. B
8. A
9. B
10. E
11. A
12. C
13. E
14. D
15. $0, \dfrac{1}{3}$
16. 81
17. $\dfrac{17}{2}$
18. -13
19. 1 (-4 is extraneous)
20. B
21. A
22. 12 degrees

Practice 50
a. D
b. C
c. No solution (9 is extraneous)
d. A
e. 4 hours

Problem Set 50
1. True
2. False
3. 8.362×10^{13}
4. 5×10^{-7}
5. 8
6. -58
7. A
8. B
9. E
10. C
11. E
12. B
13. A
14. D
15. B
16. 48
17. 4
18. 3, 2
19. 1
20. No solution (16 is extraneous)
21. D
22. 4 hours

Practice 51
a. A
b. D
c. E
d. 4 (1 is extraneous)
e. 60 pounds

Problem Set 51
1. 3,950,000,000
2. 0.0002875
3. A
4. C
5. E
6. E
7. B
8. C
9. A
10. E
11. A
12. B
13. E
14. C
15. 4
16. 7
17. $\dfrac{17}{5}$
18. 4, 2
19. 5, -5
20. No solution (2 and 1 are extraneous)
21. B
22. 37.5 pounds

Practice 52
a. 36
b. 3
c. B
d. -2 (-7 is extraneous)
e. 150 seconds

Problem Set 52
1. 30
2. 14
3. E
4. A
5. A
6. E
7. 35
8. 2
9. B
10. D
11. D
12. C
13. A
14. E
15. A
16. $-\dfrac{15}{4}$
17. 32
18. 0, -11

19. -2 (-5 is extraneous)
20. 14
21. B
22. 225 minutes

Practice 53
a. D
b. D
c. E
d. $\frac{1}{2}, 1$
e. 5 years

Problem Set 53
1. True
2. True
3. E
4. A
5. C
6. E
7. D
8. C
9. D
10. C
11. A
12. E
13. D
14. E
15. E
16. -9
17. 29
18. $0, -4$
19. $\frac{3}{2}$
20. $\frac{1}{3}, 1$
21. E
22. 6 years

Practice 54
a. C
b. 12
c. 4 (1 is extraneous)
d. E
e. 17 feet

Problem Set 54
1. True
2. True
3. -39
4. -5
5. A
6. E
7. D
8. E
9. C
10. D
11. E
12. C
13. A
14. B
15. E
16. A
17. 2
18. -1
19. 9 (1 is extraneous)
20. B
21. 31 feet

Practice 55
a. D
b. E
c. C
d. A
e. 100

Problem Set 55
1. 8.205×10^6
2. 9×10^{-2}
3. B
4. A
5. A
6. C
7. D
8. B

9. B
10. B
11. A
12. C
13. A
14. E
15. -2
16. 33
17. $-\frac{3}{5}$
18. 0, 2
19. D
20. E
21. 91

Practice 56
a. Real solutions
b. Complex solutions
c. 6 (-2 is extraneous)
d. B
e. 112

Problem Set 56
1. True
2. True
3. Real solutions
4. Complex solutions
5. D
6. A
7. E
8. A
9. B
10. D
11. A
12. E
13. A
14. E
15. B
16. 25
17. -3
18. 4 (-1 is extraneous)
19. B
20. E
21. 126

CHAPTER 9

Practice 57
a. E
b. D
c. 0, −1, −3
d. 4, 1, 0
e. $32

Problem Set 57
1. −2
2. −13
3. Complex solutions
4. Real solutions
5. B
6. A
7. C
8. C
9. A
10. B
11. A
12. C
13. D
14. E
15. A
16. $-\dfrac{4}{3}$
17. 0, −1, −2
18. 8
19. 3, 2, 0
20. A
21. $2

Practice 58
a. B
b. C
c. 6, 0, −3
d. A
e. 5 hours

Problem Set 58
1. 48,000,000
2. 0.001125

3. Complex solutions
4. Real solutions
5. E
6. D
7. B
8. C
9. B
10. E
11. C
12. B
13. C
14. D
15. $\dfrac{11}{5}$
16. 5, 0, −3
17. $-\dfrac{1}{4}$
18. −40
19. E
20. 7 hours

Practice 59
a. C
b. D
c. 0, −3, −5
d. 2, 1, −4
e. 60 seconds

Problem Set 59
1. True
2. True
3. True
4. 0
5. −2
6. Real solutions
7. Real solutions
8. B
9. A
10. D
11. A
12. E
13. B
14. B

15. E
16. 20
17. 3
18. 0, −3, −4
19. $\dfrac{21}{2}$
20. 1, −2, −3
21. 250 seconds

Practice 60
a. C
b. E
c. D
d. 5, 1, −2
e. 17

Problem Set 60
1. True
2. False
3. 1.215×10^{14}
4. 3.2×10^{-6}
5. E
6. A
7. E
8. D
9. B
10. B
11. A
12. A
13. A
14. −3
15. $0, \dfrac{1}{2}$
16. −19
17. 4, 0, −1
18. 9
19. 4, 1, −2
20. 21

Practice 61
a. D
b. C

c. 2, −1, −3
d. C
e. 58 feet

Problem Set 61

1. True
2. False
3. −0.29
4. 3.68
5. B
6. E
7. D
8. C
9. A
10. B
11. D
12. A
13. E
14. $\dfrac{11}{14}$
15. −1, −3
16. $-\dfrac{3}{2}$
17. $\dfrac{13}{5}$
18. 2, 1, −2
19. B
20. 4 feet

6. A
7. A
8. B
9. E
10. B
11. E
12. B
13. C
14. A
15. −3
16. 6
17. 2, 0, −3
18. E
19. A
20. 50 ounces

Practice 62

a. C
b. E
c. 3, 0, −4
d. D
e. 40 ounces

Problem Set 62

1. False
2. False
3. 7.52×10^{5}
4. 6.01×10^{-4}
5. E

CHAPTER 10

Practice 63
 a. A
 b. 4, 3, 0
 c. $y = -3$
 d. Yes
 e. 11 quarters

Problem Set 63
 1. True
 2. True
 3. True
 4. D
 5. E
 6. A
 7. C
 8. D
 9. A
 10. D
 11. $-\dfrac{16}{7}$
 12. -5
 13. 3, 2, 0
 14. $y = 5$
 15. $y = 7$
 16. $y = 1$
 17. Yes
 18. No
 19. Yes
 20. 14 dimes

Practice 64
 a. B
 b. $0\,(-5\text{ is extraneous})$
 c. D
 d. C
 e. $5,000

Problem Set 64
 1. True
 2. True

 3. A
 4. C
 5. E
 6. D
 7. A
 8. E
 9. 44
 10. -7
 11. $0\,(-3\text{ is extraneous})$
 12. $y = -10$
 13. $y = -1$
 14. $y = -8$
 15. No
 16. Yes
 17. Yes
 18. D
 19. A
 20. D
 21. $50,000

Practice 65
 a. and b.

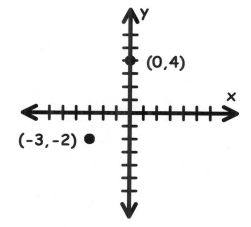

 c. C
 d. A
 e. 1.5 hours

Problem Set 65
 1. True
 2. True
 3. False

4. True

5. 7.5×10^7

6. 5.25×10^3

7. B

8. D

9. 4

10. $8, -3$

11. – 13.

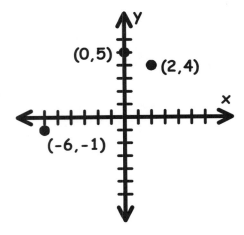

14. $y = -17$

15. $y = 25$

16. No

17. Yes

18. A

19. E

20. C

21. D

22. 6.5 hours

Practice 66

a. D

b. $4, 0, -6$

c. B

d. E

e. 48 seconds

Problem Set 66

1. False

2. True

3. True

4. 47

5. -1

6. E

7. E

8. D

9. A

10. $-\dfrac{8}{3}$

11. $\dfrac{5}{3}$

12. $5, 0, -7$

13. and 14.

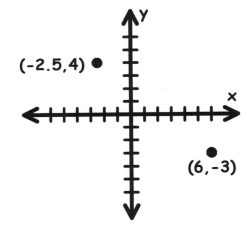

15. $y = 5$

16. $y = -\dfrac{1}{3}$

17. Yes

18. Yes

19. E

20. C

21. B

22. D

23. 380 seconds

Practice 67

a. -5

b. $+3$

c. $+2$

d. $+1$

e. 28 degrees

Problem Set 67

1. True
2. True
3. -16
4. 25
5. C
6. E
7. D
8. A
9. -5
10. $\dfrac{10}{3}$
11. C
12. $y = -22$
13. $y = -3$
14. B
15. E
16. C
17. C
18. $+4$
19. $+3$
20. $+1$
21. 20 degrees

Practice 68

a. $0, -2, -6$
b. y = 5x + 2

×	-2	-1	0	1	2	3
y	-8	-3	2	7	12	17

c. $-\dfrac{3}{5}$
d. -4
e. 5 years old

Problem Set 68

1. True
2. True
3. E
4. A
5. B
6. C

7. -8
8. $-\dfrac{5}{7}$
9. $0, -2, -5$
10. y = 6x

×	-2	-1	0	1	2	3
y	-12	-6	0	6	12	18

11. y = 4x + 1

×	-2	-1	0	1	2	3
y	-7	-3	1	5	9	13

12. A
13. D
14. B
15. E
16. -8
17. $+3$
18. $-\dfrac{2}{3}$
19. $+2$
20. -3
21. 2 years old

Practice 69

a. D
b. B
c. A
d. Slope $+2$; y-intercept $(0,-5)$
e. 25 pounds

Problem Set 69

1. True
2. True
3. D
4. E
5. B
6. D
7. A
8. 5
9. 1

10. 8, 0

11. and 12.

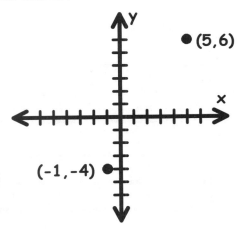

13. $y = -2$

14. $y = 6$

15. A

16. A

17. C

18. E

19. Slope $\frac{5}{7}$; y-intercept $(0, 9)$

20. Slope 3; y-intercept $(0, -6)$

21. 8 pounds

Practice 70

a. D

b. $+\frac{3}{2}$

c. B

d. A

e. $12,000

Problem Set 70

1. True

2. False

3. 9.628×10^8

4. 3.7×10^{-4}

5. A

6. E

7. $-\frac{28}{3}$

8. $\frac{3}{2}$

9. E

10. y = -5x

x	-2	-1	0	1	2	3
y	10	5	0	-5	-10	-15

11. $y = \frac{1}{2}x + 3$

x	-2	-1	0	1	2	3
y	2	$\frac{5}{2}$	3	$\frac{7}{2}$	4	$\frac{9}{2}$

12. C

13. D

14. A

15. B

16. -3

17. $\frac{4}{3}$

18. D

19. E

20. B

21. $45,000

Practice 71

a. C

b. 3, 2, 1

c. $y = 37$

d. B

e. 30 feet

Problem Set 71

1. True

2. False

3. -1

4. -2

5. D

6. E

7. E
8. A
9. 2
10. $-\dfrac{10}{3}$
11. $3, 1, -2$
12. $y = 5$
13. $y = 16$
14. E
15. A
16. $-\dfrac{2}{5}$
17. 1
18. D
19. D
20. A
21. 36 inches

11. $y = -7x + 2$

x	-2	-1	0	1	2	3
y	16	9	2	-5	-12	-19

12. Parallel
13. Perpendicular
14. Horizontal
15. B
16. E
17. -3
18. $\dfrac{3}{2}$
19. D
20. A
21. 7 hours

Practice 72

a. Perpendicular
b. Horizontal
c. C
d. D
e. 5 hours

Problem Set 72

1. True
2. True
3. E
4. B
5. E
6. B
7. 2
8. $-\dfrac{3}{5}$
9. C
10. $y = 11x$

x	-2	-1	0	1	2	3
y	-22	-11	0	11	22	33

CHAPTER 11

Practice 73
a. E
b. D
c. $-3, -5$
d. E
e. 144 seconds

Problem Set 73
1. True
2. True
3. True
4. C
5. A
6. E
7. B
8. $-\dfrac{6}{11}$
9. $\dfrac{3}{5}$
10. $-4, -5$
11. $y = 7$
12. $y = 8$
13. Parallel
14. E
15. D
16. -4
17. 3
18. B
19. A
20. 12 hours

Practice 74
a. B
b. B
c. Vertical
d. E
e. $50,000

Problem Set 74
1. True

2. False
3. True
4. C
5. D
6. 9.205×10^{6}
7. 4.3×10^{-5}
8. D
9. B
10. $\dfrac{10}{23}$
11. 2
12. D
13. $y = \dfrac{1}{2}x + 1$

x	-2	-1	0	1	2	3
y	0	$\dfrac{1}{2}$	1	$\dfrac{3}{2}$	2	$\dfrac{5}{2}$

14. $y = x^2$

x	-2	-1	0	1	2	3
y	4	1	0	1	4	9

15. Perpendicular
16. Vertical
17. $\dfrac{2}{3}$
18. -1
19. A
20. B
21. $10

Practice 75
a. $(-2, -6)$
b. E
c. A
d. C
e. 14 feet

Problem Set 75
1. False
2. True

3. (0, 0)
4. (−1, −1)
5. B
6. A
7. D
8. C
9. $\dfrac{2}{7}$
10. 30
11. $\dfrac{2}{5}$
12. $y = 10$
13. $y = 0$
14. B
15. D
16. 0
17. 10
18. C
19. E
20. 12 feet

Practice 76

a. C
b. C
c. D
d. C
e. 1.55 hours

Problem Set 76

1. A
2. B
3. − 40
4. −15
5. A
6. A
7. − 5
8. $\dfrac{5}{16}$
9. 2, 1
10. $y = −1$
11. $y = −100$
12. E

13. B
14. E
15. D
16. 3
17. $−\dfrac{2}{5}$
18. E
19. A
20. 2.06 hours

Practice 77

a. Center (5, 4); radius 9
b. E
c. A
d. A
e. 20,000 known species of crickets

Problem Set 77

1. True
2. True
3. D
4. A
5. Vertex (0, 0); opens down
6. Center: (6, 7); radius 12
7. B
8. D
9. 1
10. $\dfrac{6}{5}$
11. 2, 0
12. $y = −23.5$
13. $y = −8$
14. C
15. D
16. E
17. Undefined
18. −1
19. A
20. B
21. 192 people

Practice 78

   a. Center (2, 5); radius: 8
   b. A
   c. E
   d. D
   e. 325 nickels

Problem Set 78

   1. False
   2. True
   3. Vertex $(9,-4)$; opens up
   4. Center (3, 4); radius 7
   5. -11
   6. 2
   7. E
   8. D
   9. -2
   10. 3
   11. -4, -5
   12. $y = 80$
   13. $y = 17$
   14. B
   15. E
   16. A
   17. A
   18. C
   19. $+3$
   20. $-\dfrac{1}{6}$
   21. 120 dimes

Practice 79

   a. Center $(-4,-3)$; radius 4
   b. Center $(0,0)$; vertices $(6,0)$, $(-6,0)$
   c. C
   d. A
   e. 25 ounces

Problem Set 79

   1. True
   2. True
   3. C

   4. B
   5. Center $(-3,-2)$; radius 3
   6. Center $(0,0)$; vertices $(5,0)$, $(-5,0)$
   7. D
   8. C
   9. $\dfrac{6}{7}$
   10. $-\dfrac{1}{2}$
   11. E
   12. $y = -2.75$
   13. $y = 16$
   14. D
   15. E
   16. B
   17. Slope $-\dfrac{5}{8}$; y-intercept $(0,7)$
   18. Slope $\dfrac{1}{2}$; y-intercept $(0,0)$
   19. Parallel
   20. Horizontal
   21. 60 ounces

Practice 80

   a. Vertex $(-2,-5)$; opens up
   b. Center $(0,0)$; vertices $(0, 7)$, $(0, -7)$
   c. B
   d. E
   e. 60 feet

Problem Set 80

   1. True
   2. False
   3. Vertex $(-2,-8)$; opens up
   4. Center $(7,-1)$; radius 9
   5. Center $(0,0)$; vertices $(0,4)$, $(0,-4)$
   6. B
   7. A
   8. 1
   9. 4 (1 is extraneous)

10. D
11. $y = 14$
12. $y = 13$
13. C
14. E
15. D
16. E
17. B
18. $-\dfrac{2}{3}$
19. -4
20. 100 feet

Practice 81

a. Center $(0,0)$; vertices $(7,0)$, $(-7,0)$; opens left and right
b. C
c. B
d. Slope 0; y-intercept $(0,-2)$
e. $7,000

Problem Set 81

1. True
2. True
3. D
4. B
5. Center $(-3,9)$; radius $\sqrt{21}$
6. Vertex $(0,5)$; opens down
7. Center $(0,0)$; vertices $(5,0)$, $(-5,0)$; opens left and right
8. A
9. B
10. $-\dfrac{1}{2}$
11. 2, 0
12. $y = 8$
13. $y = 2$
14. C
15. D
16. A
17. Slope 4; y-intercept $(0,-8)$

18. Slope 0; y-intercept $(0,-1)$
19. E
20. A
21. $10,000

Practice 82

a. $\sqrt{34}$
b. Center $(2,3)$; vertices $(2,7)$, $(2,-1)$; opens up and down
c. A
d. D
e. 93

Problem Set 82

1. True
2. True
3. $2\sqrt{13}$
4. Center $(0,0)$; radius 10
5. Center $(0,0)$; vertices $(12,0)$, $(-12,0)$
6. Center $(1,5)$; vertices $(1,8)$, $(1,2)$; opens up and down
7. B
8. E
9. 3
10. $\dfrac{2}{3}$
11. $y = -80$
12. $y = 2$
13. E
14. B
15. C
16. E
17. C
18. $+\dfrac{3}{2}$
19. $-\dfrac{1}{4}$
20. 91

CHAPTER 12

Practice 83

a. $2\sqrt{17}$
b. D
c. $A = 25$
d. B
e. 2.5 hours

Problem Set 83

1. True
2. True
3. True
4. E
5. A
6. $4\sqrt{5}$
7. Vertex $(0,0)$; opens up
8. Center $(11,12)$; radius 5
9. D
10. C
11. B
12. -1
13. 3, 0
14. $y = -137$
15. $A = 24$
16. C
17. A
18. Slope $\dfrac{4}{5}$; y-intercept $(0, \dfrac{1}{4})$
19. Slope $\dfrac{1}{2}$; y-intercept $(0,0)$
20. C
21. B
22. 1.5 hours

Practice 84

a. Vertex $(-1,3)$; opens up
b. E
c. A
d. C
e. 24 degrees

Problem Set 84

1. False
2. True
3. 0
4. -1
5. $\sqrt{85}$
6. Center $(0,0)$; vertices $(7,0)$, $(-7,0)$
7. Vertex $(-1,4)$; opens up
8. E
9. C
10. $\dfrac{96}{7}$
11. $9, -4$
12. $V = 320$
13. $z = 30$
14. C
15. D
16. B
17. D
18. $-\dfrac{1}{3}$
19. $+5$
20. 16 degrees

Practice 85

a. Center $(1,3)$; vertices $(5,3)$; $(-3,3)$
b. E
c. A
d. A
e. 540 minutes

Problem Set 85

1. True
2. True
3. False
4. 1.653×10^{19}
5. 6×10^{3}
6. Vertex $(0,0)$; opens down
7. Center $(2,1)$; vertices $(5,1)$, $(-1,1)$
8. B
9. C
10. 9

11. 8 (2 is extraneous)
12. D
13. $L = -36$
14. $s = -2$
15. A
16. E
17. E
18. C
19. $+\dfrac{3}{5}$
20. -6
21. 180 hours

Practice 86

a. Center $(-3, -4)$; radius $\sqrt{21}$
b. D
c. A
d. A
e. 14

Problem Set 86

1. True
2. False
3. 3.8×10^{10}
4. 1.95×10^{-3}
5. $\sqrt{61}$
6. Parallel
7. Center $(-1, -8)$; radius $\sqrt{19}$
8. B
9. A
10. C
11. B
12. 2
13. 5
14. A
15. $z = -33$
16. E
17. B
18. B
19. E
20. E

21. C
22. 18

Practice 87

a. B
b. A
c. B
d. A
e. 988 lefties

Problem Set 87

1. E
2. C
3. Perpendicular
4. Horizontal
5. Center $(0, 0)$; vertices $(9, 0)$, $(-9, 0)$
6. A
7. D
8. D
9. E
10. D
11. $\dfrac{4}{7}$
12. $\dfrac{5}{11}$
13. 2, 0
14. $f = 9$
15. D
16. C
17. D
18. $-\dfrac{2}{3}$
19. $+5$
20. 323 wraparounds

Practice 88

a. D
b. A
c. E
d. E
e. 1.5 pounds

Problem Set 88

1. True
2. True
3. 1.675×10^{-8}
4. 3.4×10^{-6}
5. $\sqrt{13}$
6. Vertical
7. Center $(0, 0)$; radius $\sqrt{31}$
8. C
9. E
10. C
11. D
12. D
13. E
14. A
15. C
16. $\dfrac{17}{4}$
17. E
18. $z = 52$
19. B
20. B
21. A
22. 4.8 ounces

Practice 89

a. A
b. D
c. C
d. D
e. 1.63 hours

Problem Set 89

1. True
2. True
3. 2.9106×10^{7}
4. 5×10^{-9}
5. $\sqrt{61}$
6. Horizontal
7. Center $(9, 4)$; radius 5
8. A
9. C

10. B
11. E
12. C
13. C
14. B
15. $-\dfrac{8}{5}$
16. 4
17. $S = 125.6$
18. B
19. $-\dfrac{1}{2}$
20. $\dfrac{1}{3}$
21. 2.08 hours

Practice 90

a. C
b. E
c. A
d. B
e. $10,000

Problem Set 90

1. D
2. A
3. Perpendicular
4. Center $(0, 0)$; vertices $(8, 0)$, $(-8, 0)$
5. B
6. D
7. D
8. C
9. C
10. A
11. E
12. D
13. A
14. $-\dfrac{5}{3}$
15. $0, -4$
16. $p = 30$
17. E
18. C

19. E
20. E
21. A
22. $20,000

Practice 91
a. B
b. A
c. D
d. A
e. 50 feet

Problem Set 91
1. 2.548×10^{18}
2. 2.1×10^5
3. 5
4. Vertical
5. Vertex $(8, 3)$; opens up
6. E
7. A
8. E
9. C
10. D
11. E
12. B
13. D
14. A
15. 28
16. $-1, -3$
17. $y = -10$
18. E
19. D
20. B
21. 140 feet

Practice 92
a. D
b. C
c. D
d. A
e. 1.25 hours

Problem Set 92
1. 24
2. -1
3. Parallel
4. Center $(-7, 2)$; radius 10
5. D
6. B
7. C
8. B
9. A
10. E
11. D
12. A
13. B
14. 2
15. 8
16. $z = 4$
17. E
18. B
19. D
20. E
21. C
22. 1.75 hours

Practice 93
a. C
b. E
c. B
d. C
e. 15 degrees

Problem Set 93
1. 7.95×10^8
2. 3.2×10^{-10}
3. $\sqrt{10}$
4. Horizontal
5. Center $(0, 0)$; vertices $(4, 0)$, $(-4, 0)$; opens left and right
6. A
7. C
8. E
9. E
10. A

11. B

12. A

13. D

14. A

15. -3

16. 5 (2 is extraneous)

17. $u = 144$

18. D

19. E

20. B

21. 12 degrees

CHAPTER 13

Practice 94

a. C
b. D
c. $x = 3$, $y = 2$
d. $x = 7$, $y = -2$
e. 1.2 hours

Problem Set 94

1. True
2. True
3. A
4. B
5. Parallel
6. Center $(0, 0)$; radius $\sqrt{7}$
7. D
8. D
9. E
10. E
11. A
12. B
13. C
14. $\dfrac{11}{2}$
15. C
16. $z = 1$
17. E
18. E
19. A
20. $x = 4$, $y = 5$
21. $x = 6$, $y = -3$
22. 3.6 hours

Practice 95

a. E
b. D
c. $x = -4$, $y = 1$
d. $x = 1$, $y = 1$
e. 12 years old

Problem Set 95

1. 85
2. -4
3. $5\sqrt{2}$
4. Vertex $(0, 0)$; opens down
5. A
6. A
7. C
8. D
9. E
10. B
11. B
12. A
13. 12
14. E
15. $Q = 45$
16. B
17. A
18. D
19. $x = 21$, $y = 28$
20. $x = -5$, $y = 1$
21. $x = 1$, $y = -1$
22. 20 years old

Practice 96

a. D
b. C
c. B
d. $x = -2$, $y = -5$
e. 3 hours

Problem Set 96

1. False
2. True
3. 2.736×10^{-7}
4. 5.625×10^{5}
5. Perpendicular
6. Center $(0, 0)$; vertices $(7, 0)$ $(-7, 0)$
7. D
8. A
9. E
10. D

11. B
12. A
13. −19
14. $\dfrac{13}{2}$
15. $F = 292.8$
16. B
17. C
18. D
19. $x = 2$, $y = 2$
20. $x = 1$, $y = 3$
21. $x = -3$, $y = -8$
22. 6 hours

Practice 97
a. E
b. $x = \dfrac{1}{2}$, $y = 3$
c. B
d. A
e. 9, 15

Problem Set 97
1. True
2. True
3. 5×10^9
4. 4.73×10^{-5}
5. $\sqrt{41}$
6. Center $(5, 4)$; radius 9
7. B
8. A
9. B
10. B
11. A
12. D
13. A
14. 7
15. 0, −5
16. $A = 40$
17. E
18. $x = 1$, $y = 4$

19. $x = \dfrac{1}{3}$, $y = -2$
20. D
21. E
22. 16, 21

Practice 98
a. Vertex $(0, 2)$; opens up
b. C
c. $x = 2$, $y = 5$
d. 4 solution pairs
e. 30 quarters

Problem Set 98
1. True
2. False
3. −2
4. 9
5. $\sqrt{34}$
6. Vertex $(0, 4)$; opens up
7. D
8. A
9. E
10. B
11. B
12. C
13. $\dfrac{8}{3}$
14. 7, 3
15. D
16. A
17. $x = 5$, $y = -1$
18. $x = 1$, $y = 3$
19. 2 solution pairs
20. 4 solution pairs
21. 60 dimes

Practice 99
a. B
b. $x = 3$, $y = 3$
c. $x = 3$, $y = 9$ and $x = 1$, $y = 1$

d. $x = -4$, $y = -18$ and $x = -1$, $y = -3$

e. 29, 8

Problem Set 99

1. Parallel
2. Center $(1, -3)$; radius 4
3. A
4. C
5. D
6. E
7. A
8. B
9. Yes
10. No
11. -2
12. $0, -7$
13. $y = 48$
14. E
15. D
16. B
17. $x = 9$, $y = 0$
18. $x = 2$, $y = 2$
19. $x = 2$, $y = 4$ and $x = 1$, $y = 1$
20. $x = -2$, $y = -1$ and $x = -1$, $y = 1$
21. 42, 68

Practice 100

a. Center $(1, 3)$; vertices $(7, 3)$, $(-5, 3)$

b. C

c. $x = 5$, $y = -20$ and $x = 1$, $y = -4$

d. $x = 7$, $y = 5$ and $x = -7$, $y = 5$ and $x = 7$, $y = -5$ and $x = -7$, $y = -5$

e. a) $16 for each butterfly net
b) $18 for each magnifying glass

Problem Set 100

1. 1.512×10^{17}
2. 5×10^{-4}
3. $\sqrt{13}$
4. Center $(1, 2)$; vertices $(9, 2)$, $(-7, 2)$
5. A

6. D
7. D
8. E
9. C
10. E
11. B
12. -3
13. E
14. $d = 156.8$
15. D
16. $x = -1$, $y = -8$
17. $x = 4$, $y = 5$
18. $x = 5$, $y = -30$ and $x = 1$, $y = -6$
19. $x = 4$, $y = 6$ and $x = -4$, $y = 6$ and $x = 4$, $y = -6$ and $x = -4$, $y = -6$
20. a) $30 for each pair of sneakers
b) $35 for each pair of pants

Practice 101

a. E

b. $x = 3$, $y = 18$ and $x = -1.5$, $y = 4.5$

c. $x = 6$, $y = 8$ and $x = -6$, $y = -8$

d. $x = 3$, $y = 1$, $z = 2$

e. 25 ounces

Problem Set 101

1. True
2. False
3. D
4. B
5. A
6. C
7. E
8. A
9. $\dfrac{3}{4}$
10. 2
11. $w = -35$
12. B
13. C
14. A
15. $x = 5$, $y = -10$

16. $x = 7$, $y = -2$
17. $x = -1$, $y = 2$ and $x = 2$, $y = 8$
18. $x = 3$, $y = 4$ and $x = -3$, $y = -4$
19. $x = 2$, $y = 1$, $z = -1$
20. 20 ounces

Practice 102

a. D
b. $x = -8$, $y = -4$ and $x = -1$, $y = 3$
c. $x = 3$, $y = 4$ and $x = -3$, $y = 4$ and
$x = 3$, $y = -4$ and $x = -3$, $y = -4$
d. $a = 2$, $b = 2$, $c = -3$
e. 13, 42

Problem Set 102

1. 5.893×10^7
2. 1.8×10^{-3}
3. E
4. A
5. B
6. C
7. No
8. Yes
9. $-\dfrac{16}{3}$
10. E
11. $z = -7$
12. B
13. C
14. A
15. $x = \dfrac{1}{3}$, $y = 4$
16. $x = -5$, $y = -11$
17. $x = -6$, $y = -3$ and $x = -1$, $y = 2$
18. $x = 2$, $y = 3$ and $x = -2$, $y = 3$ and
$x = 2$, $y = -3$ and $x = -2$, $y = -3$
19. $a = 1$, $b = 3$, $c = -1$
20. 16, 54

CHAPTER 14

Practice 103

a. D
b. D
c. C
d. E
e. a) $4 for each roll of duct tape
b) $30 for each radio

Problem Set 103

1. True
2. True
3. E
4. B
5. A
6. C
7. C
8. 14
9. 6
10. $x = 5$, $y = -3$
11. $x = 4$, $y = 1$
12. No solutions
13. $x = 2$, $y = 1$
14. B
15. A
16. E
17. B
18. D
19. A
20. B
21. a) $4 for each deodorizer
b) $6 for each mildew remover

Practice 104

a. D
b. $x = 4$, $y = 2$ and $x = -4$, $y = 2$ and $x = 4$, $y = -2$ and $x = -4$, $y = -2$
c. $x = 2$, $y = 1$, $z = 1$
d. C
e. 1,426 late-sleepers

Problem Set 104

1. $\sqrt{117}$
2. Center $(0, 0)$; vertices $(5, 0)$, $(-5, 0)$; opens left and right
3. D
4. C
5. B
6. A
7. E
8. Yes
9. No
10. 5
11. $\dfrac{9}{2}$
12. $F = \dfrac{1}{2}$ or 0.5
13. B
14. $x = 6$, $y = -7$
15. $x = 1$, $y = 4$
16. $x = 3$, $y = 2$ and $x = -3$, $y = 2$ and $x = 3$, $y = -2$ and $x = -3$, $y = -2$
17. $x = 3$, $y = 1$, $z = 2$
18. E
19. B
20. 1,508 trend-setters

Practice 105

a. $x = 1$, $y = 3$, $z = -4$
b. C
c. A
d. D
e. $3

Problem Set 105

1. True
2. True
3. True
4. A
5. C
6. B
7. $\dfrac{5}{2}$

8. 5, 0
9. E
10. C
11. C
12. B
13. $x = 3$, $y = 6$
14. $x = 5$, $y = \dfrac{2}{3}$
15. $x = 1$, $y = 2$, $z = -3$
16. B
17. C
18. B
19. A
20. B
21. $240

Practice 106
a. B
b. $x = 1$, $y = 5$ and $x = \dfrac{3}{2}$, $y = \dfrac{15}{2}$
c. E
d. B
e. More than 20 vacuums

Problem Set 106
1. -5
2. -6
3. B
4. A
5. C
6. E
7. D
8. -2
9. 3, 1
10. 4
11. A
12. $x = 6$, $y = 1$
13. $x = 7$, $y = 2$
14. $x = 1$, $y = 7$ and $x = \dfrac{5}{2}$, $y = \dfrac{35}{2}$
15. C
16. E
17. C

18. A
19. C
20. B
21. More than 100 wristwatches

Practice 107
a. D
b. $x = -1$, $y = 5$, $z = -3$
c. D
d. E
e. a) $6 for each chicken biscuit bag
   b) $5 for each parmesan biscuit bag

Problem Set 107
1. 3.88×10^{15}
2. 6.4×10^{5}
3. E
4. B
5. C
6. Yes
7. Yes
8. 3
9. $\dfrac{5}{8}$
10. E
11. B
12. E
13. B
14. $x = 7$, $y = -14$
15. $x = 4$, $y = 15$
16. $x = -2$, $y = 6$, $z = -4$
17. A
18. C
19. B
20. C
21. a) $50 for each lifejacket
    b) $40 for each paddle

Practice 108
a. $x = 3$, $y = 4$ and $x = 3$, $y = -4$ and $x = -3$, $y = 4$ and $x = -3$, $y = -4$
b. A
c. B
d. D
e. 45 hours

Problem Set 108
1. True
2. False
3. B
4. A
5. E
6. E
7. $\dfrac{1}{3}$
8. D
9. $a = 18$
10. D
11. $x = 2$, $y = 24$
12. $x = -3$, $y = 1$
13. $x = 3$, $y = 5$ and $x = 3$, $y = -5$ and $x = -3$, $y = 5$ and $x = -3$, $y = -5$
14. C
15. E
16. E
17. C
18. C
19. A
20. A
21. B
22. 144 hours

Practice 109
a. $x = -7$, $y = 1$, $z = -5$
b. C
c. E
d. C
e. More than 20,000 onion peelers.

Problem Set 109
1. False
2. True
3. Perpendicular
4. Vertex $(2, 4)$; opens up
5. D
6. B
7. $-\dfrac{6}{7}$
8. 2, 0
9. A
10. C
11. $x = -9$, $y = -4$
12. $x = -4$, $y = 1$, $z = -3$
13. C
14. D
15. B
16. C
17. E
18. E
19. A
20. B
21. E
22. More than 30,000 whistles

Practice 110
a. $x = 5$, $y = 77$ and $x = -\dfrac{1}{3}$, $y = \dfrac{7}{3}$
b. D
c. A
d. E
e. a) $8 for each coffee mug
   b) $14 for each t-shirt

Problem Set 110
1. True
2. True
3. C
4. A
5. A
6. B
7. E

8. $\dfrac{21}{10}$

9. 3

10. $z = -45$

11. D

12. $x = -8$, $y = 3$

13. $x = 3$, $y = 28$ and $x = -\dfrac{1}{3}$, $y = \dfrac{4}{3}$

14. C

15. D

16. E

17. E

18. B

19. D

20. A

21. a) $16 for each gizmo
    b) $9 for each thingamajig

17. E

18. D

19. A

20. C

21. B

22. 9 hours

Practice 111

a. C

b. $x = 2$, $y = 6$, $z = -2$

c. D

d. D

e. 7 hours

Problem Set 111

1. 4.89×10^8

2. 2.7×10^{-7}

3. $\sqrt{41}$

4. Center $(-2, 9)$; radius 12

5. B

6. A

7. No

8. Yes

9. 6

10. 4, -2

11. $x = 12$, $y = 3$

12. $x = 3$, $y = 7$, $z = -1$

13. B

14. B

15. A

16. A

CHAPTER 15

Practice 112
a. 13
b. 4
c. $x = \dfrac{12}{5}$, $y = \dfrac{16}{5}$ and $x = -4$, $y = 0$
d. D
e. More than 4,000 books

Problem Set 112
1. True
2. True
3. True
4. 6
5. 11
6. 5
7. A
8. D
9. C
10. 2
11. 3, −4
12. $r = -4$
13. B
14. $x = -3$, $y = -5$
15. $x = -4$, $y = 3$ and $x = 5$, $y = 0$
16. A
17. E
18. E
19. D
20. A
21. B
22. D
23. More than 20,000 books

Practice 113
a. $x = 2$, $y = 9$, $z = 0$
b. D
c. 19, −11
d. 8, −1
e. a) $28 for each bat
   b) $4 for each baseball

Problem Set 113
1. True
2. True
3. 8
4. $\dfrac{1}{4}$
5. 9
6. C
7. E
8. −40
9. $\dfrac{26}{9}$
10. B
11. D
12. A
13. C
14. $x = 8$, $y = -5$
15. $x = 1$, $y = 8$, $z = 0$
16. B
17. E
18. B
19. 7, −7
20. 14, −8
21. 4, −1
22. a) $0.50 for each geranium
    b) $1 for each tulip bulb

Practice 114
a. E
b. C
c. 4, 0
d. No solutions
e. 300 seconds

Problem Set 114
1. False
2. False
3. 0
4. 1
5. C
6. A
7. B
8. A

9. $\dfrac{44}{7}$

10. $3, -3$

11. $V = 268.16$

12. D

13. $x = -2$, $y = -2$

14. $x = 3$, $y = 5$ and $x = -1$, $y = -3$

15. D

16. E

17. B

18. A

19. $17, -9$

20. $9, -5$

21. No solutions

22. 1,350 seconds

18. $13, 7$

19. -3

20. C

21. A

22. a) $12 for each pack of diapers

   b) $3 for each jar of honey

Practice 115

a. $x = 1$, $y = 4$, $z = -2$

b. -4

c. D

d. B

e. a) $60 for each pair of long-johns

   b) $80 for each pair of mittens

Problem Set 115

1. True

2. False

3. Parallel

4. Center $(0, 0)$; vertices $(0, 6)$, $(0, -6)$;
   opens up and down

5. C

6. E

7. 14

8. B

9. Yes

10. Yes

11. $x = 3$, $y = -2$

12. $x = 2$, $y = 3$, $z = -1$

13. D

14. C

15. D

16. E

17. $4, -4$

CHAPTER 16

Practice 116
a. No
b. No
c. D
d. D
e. $350,000

Problem Set 116
1. True
2. False
3. 9
4. 23
5. C
6. E
7. -21
8. A
9. No solutions
10. $x = 6$, $y = 9$ and $x = 6$, $y = -9$ and $x = -6$, $y = 9$ and $x = -6$, $y = -9$
11. Yes
12. No
13. Yes
14. No
15. Yes
16. A
17. B
18. B
19. E
20. E
21. D
22. $50.00

Practice 117
a. 27
b. C
c. B
d. B
e. 150 seconds

Problem Set 117
1. True
2. True
3. 3
4. 8
5. D
6. C
7. C
8. D
9. A
10. D
11. 5
12. B
13. $x = 7$, $y = 6$
14. $x = 4$, $y = 5$, $z = -1$
15. A
16. B
17. B
18. B
19. E
20. D
21. 160 seconds

Practice 118
a. E
b. A
c. B
d. C
e. 135 people

Problem Set 118
1. True
2. True
3. $5\sqrt{2}$
4. vertex = (0,0); parabola opens down
5. D
6. C
7. 9
8. 14
9. A
10. C
11. $x = 3$, $y = 2$
12. $x = -2$, $y = 2$

13. D
14. A
15. A
16. A
17. B
18. D
19. C
20. E
21. B
22. D
23. 322 people

Practice 119

a. No solution
b. C
c. No
d. C
e. a) $40 for each wiggler
   b) $70 for each husky musky

Problem Set 119

1. True
2. True
3. −20
4. −128
5. −33
6. $\dfrac{5}{3}$
7. D
8. A
9. $w = 2$
10. D
11. 4 and -5
12. No Solution
13. E
14. D
15. B
16. C
17. A
18. No
19. C
20. No

21. A
22. a) $20 for each small pillow
    b) $45 for each large pillow

Practice 120

a. 3
b. k(x)

x	-2	-1	0	1	2
y	-8	-2	0	-2	-8

c. B
d. C
e. $1.20

Problem Set 120

1. True
2. True
3. Center = (0,0); Radius = $\sqrt{17}$
4. Center = $(-4,-8)$; Vertices = $(-4, -12)$, $(-4,-4)$; Opens up and down
5. D
6. A
7. C
8. A
9. E
10. 9
11. 2
12. C
13. E
14. g(x)

x	-2	-1	0	1	2
y	-16	-4	0	-4	-16

15. q(x)

x	2	1	0	-1	-2
y	$\frac{1}{4}$	$\frac{1}{2}$	1	2	4

16. E
17. C
18. A
19. D
20. $w = -13$

21. C
22. $1.00

Practice 121

a. A
b. C
c. B
d. $y = 103$
e. 6 years

Problem Set 121

1. True
2. True
3. E
4. E
5. A
6. C
7. -2
8. 8
9. 6
10. E
11. D
12. C
13. A
14. B
15. D
16. E
17. B
18. A
19. A
20. $y = -53$
21. $y = 10,953$
22. 5 years

Practice 122

a. 530.45
b. E
c. E
d. D
e. 28,138

Problem Set 122

1. True
2. False
3. False
4. 1,225.04
5. 1,402.55
6. B
7. C
8. A
9. g(x)

x	-2	-1	0	1	2
y	-32	-8	0	-8	-32

10. k(x)

x	2	1	0	-1	-2
y	$\frac{1}{9}$	$\frac{1}{3}$	0	3	9

11. C
12. D
13. $x = 10$, $y = 1$
14. $x = 4$, $y = 3$, $z = 2$
15. C
16. A
17. C
18. A
19. A
20. B
21. E
22. 33,122

Practice 123

a. A
b. B
c. $x = 3$, $y = 4$, $z = 5$
d. E
e. $11,431

Problem Set 123

1. True
2. True
3. D
4. E

5. B

6. $\dfrac{2}{7}$

7. -8 and 6

8. 28

9. $-\dfrac{1}{10}$

10. B
11. A
12. C
13. E
14. E
15. A
16. C
17. $x = 4$, $y = 12$ and $x = -1$, $y = -3$
18. $x = 2$, $y = 3$, $z = 4$
19. C
20. A
21. D
22. $11,219

Practice 124

a. 5
b. 2.6314
c. 5
d. 1.2041
e. A

Problem Set 124

1. True
2. False
3. 2
4. 3
5. 4
6. 1.1761
7. 0.3010
8. 2.5551
9. 4
10. 1.1461
11. C
12. D
13. B
14. 8

15. 3
16. -10, -1
17. C
18. E
19. A
20. D
21. D
22. E

Practice 125

a. 8
b. 2.4456
c. -0.5479
d. 0.7018
e. 28.0110 years

Problem Set 125

1. True
2. True
3. 1
4. 0
5. 7
6. 2.9304
7. 1.2788
8. 3.6035
9. B
10. E

11. $\dfrac{3}{4}$

12. -1
13. 2.5105
14. 0.1826
15. 0.3786
16. $\sqrt{58}$
17. Center (4,2); Radius 11
18. -21
19. 20
20. E
21. B
22. 11.8957 years

CHAPTER 17

Practice 126

a. $x = 2$
b. mean = 517.5, median = 520, mode = 530
c. C
d. -0.8955
e. 12 hours

Problem Set 126

1. False
2. False
3. False
4. -44
5. 2
6. 2
7. 3
8. 3.2586
9. 1.6335
10. D
11. B
12. 2
13. $-4, -2$
14. mean = 20, median = 19, mode = 16
15. mean = 538.75, median = 535, mode = 540
16. C
17. B
18. E
19. C
20. 2.6425
21. -1.1383
22. 15 hours

Practice 127

a. Center $(-4, -23)$; Opens up
b. mean = 4.8, median = 4.6, mode = 4.5
c. Range = 33, Standard deviation = 10.29
d. 0.1658
e. 8 quarters

Problem Set 127

1. True
2. True
3. C
4. A
5. Center $(-3, -15)$; Opens up
6. Center $(0,0)$; Vertices $(6,0)$, $(-6,0)$
7. 50.31
8. 141.51
9. 2.7497
10. 1.9956
11. mean = 27, median = 26, mode = 25
12. mean = 4.3, median = 4.25, mode = 4.2
13. Range = 5, Standard deviation = 1.59
14. Range = 19, Standard deviation = 6.23
15. 144
16. E
17. B
18. B
19. D
20. 2.4683
21. 0.5805
22. 11 nickels

Practice 128

a. 15
b. Range = 6, Standard deviation = 2.14
c. 53 to 61
d. 193 to 245
e. 18 feet

Problem Set 128

1. True
2. True
3. B
4. C
5. -8
6. 6, 2
7. B
8. D
9. B
10. E
11. E
12. 3

13. 2
14. A
15. C
16. 28
17. 24
18. Range = 9, Standard deviation = 3.12
19. Range = 23, Standard deviation = 6.78
20. 31 to 47
21. 677 to 773
22. 24 feet

Practice 129

a. 8.9889
b. 87
c. 13,600
d. A
e. 12, 14

Problem Set 129

1. True
2. False
3. False
4. 4.4×10^{-9}
5. 6.0×10^{8}
6. D
7. C
8. D
9. E
10. A
11. E
12. 3.7227
13. 2.8635
14. B
15. C
16. 82
17. 136
18. 190
19. B
20. A
21. B
22. 16 and 18

Practice 130

a. B
b. A
c. $\dfrac{11}{15}$
d. $\dfrac{1}{6}$
e. width = 24

Problem Set 130

1. False
2. True
3. 1
4. 0
5. 4
6. $6^{\frac{5}{6}}$
7. $2^{\frac{1}{20}}$
8. 9
9. $-\dfrac{1}{18}$
10. 0, −32
11. 4, 5
12. $d = -144$
13. A
14. B
15. A
16. C
17. B
18. $\dfrac{2}{7}$
19. $\dfrac{5}{7}$
20. $\dfrac{1}{4}$
21. $\dfrac{1}{9}$
22. width = 5

Practice 131

a. E
b. 1,757,600

c. 336
d. 126
e. 87,625 people

Problem Set 131

1. True
2. True
3. C
4. B
5. $\dfrac{2}{13}$
6. $\dfrac{1}{8}$
7. 510
8. 349,300
9. Yes
10. No
11. D
12. A
13. A
14. B
15. A
16. B
17. B
18. 17,576,000
19. 24
20. 60
21. 35
22. 70,416 people

Practice 132

a. 6,720
b. $\dfrac{1}{216}$
c. $\dfrac{1}{240}$
d. $\dfrac{21}{26}$
e. 24 degrees

Problem Set 132

1. True
2. True

3. False
4. D
5. A
6. $\dfrac{2}{9}$
7. $-\dfrac{38}{5}$
8. $\dfrac{23}{5}$
9. 362,880
10. 2,520
11. 126
12. B
13. B
14. E
15. B
16. D
17. A
18. C
19. $\dfrac{1}{16}$
20. $\dfrac{1}{240}$
21. $\dfrac{5}{26}$
22. 30 degrees

Practice 133

a. $\dfrac{1}{50,653}$
b. 10.5%
c. $450
d. $0.50; No
e. $300,000; No

Problem Set 133

1. True
2. True
3. −6
4. 21
5. E
6. C
7. 95,040

8. 120

9. $\dfrac{1}{1,369}$

10. 2.8344

11. 2.3802

12. Vertex (0,0); Opens down

13. Center (0,0) Vertices (0, −5), (0,5);
    Opens up and down

14. E

15. A

16. 38

17. E

18. 3.5%

19. 2.5%

20. $180

21. $0.80; No

22. $600,000; Yes

CHAPTER 18

Practice 134
a. 117,649
b. B
c. E
d. $63
e. $1,864

Problem Set 134
1. True
2. True
3. False
4. A
5. C
6. E
7. $-19, -28, -37$
8. 512; 2,048; 8,192
9. 70
10. 6,561
11. E
12. D
13. 120
14. 56
15. 27%
16. $2.40
17. -4
18. -1
19. D
20. A
21. D
22. $3,200

Practice 135
a. B
b. E
c. $x = -5$, $y = 2$, $z = 4$
d. 51
e. $15,000; no

Problem Set 135
1. True
2. True
3. D
4. C
5. A
6. 2
7. 0
8. 3
9. 17.5, 21, 24.5
10. $\dfrac{1}{16}, \dfrac{1}{32}, \dfrac{1}{64}$
11. -71
12. D
13. $+6$
14. -3
15. E
16. $x = -4$, $y = 1$, $z = 3$
17. 34
18. 285
19. 23.33%
20. $\dfrac{1}{32}$
21. 60
22. $75,000; Yes

Practice 136
a. C
b. A
c. D
d. C
e. $2,900

Problem Set 136
1. True
2. True
3. E
4. E
5. D
6. B
7. E
8. B
9. B
10. A
11. 5.5, 10, 14.5
12. -16, 32, -64
13. 117
14. B

15. 6, −6

16. $2, -\dfrac{3}{2}$

17. $-\dfrac{5}{12}$

18. E

19. $\dfrac{1}{1,296}$

20. 1,320

21. 3,003

22. $2,700

21. $x = -7$, $y = 1$

22. 8 hours

Practice 137

a. Center (0,0); Vertices (-5, 0), (5,0);
   Opens left and right

b. B

c. 187

d. $x = -9$, $y = 5$

e. 7 hours

Problem Set 137

1. True

2. True

3. D

4. A

5. E

6. Parallel

7. Center (0,0); Vertices (-7,0), (7,0);
   Opens left and right

8. A

9. A

10. D

11. A

12. B

13. 325

14. D

15. B

16. E

17. 0

18. −2

19. −132

20. $x = 4$, $y = -3$

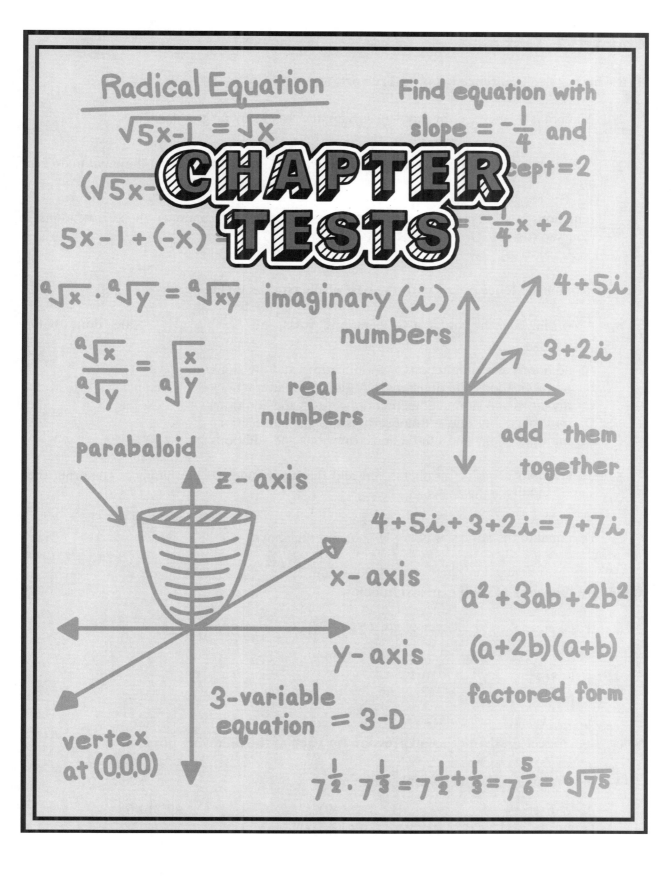

Chapter 1 Test

Tell whether each sentence below is True or False.

1. Algebra is a language for problem solving that has its own "grammar."
(2)

2. Addition and multiplication are inverse operations, which means that they will undo each
(3) other.

3. Equations with more than one operation are solved by undoing those operations in
(3) reverse order.

Complete each sentence below with the best of the choices given.

4. According to the order of operations rules, all _____ are done before
(2) _____.

    A. additions and subtractions; multiplications and divisions
    B. multiplications and divisions; additions and subtractions
    C. divisions and subtractions; multiplications and additions
    D. multiplications and additions; divisions and subtractions
    E. multiplications and subtractions; divisions and additions

5. To add two negative numbers, you add the magnitudes of the numbers (ignoring their
(5) signs) and make the answer _____.

    A. positive   B. zero   C. negative
    D. equal to the larger number   E. none of the above

Calculate the value of each expression below.

6. $8 \cdot 2 + 9$ **7.** $5(8 - 2)$ **8.** $(11)(-4)$
(2)   (2)   (5)

9. $-21 - 16$ **10.** $\dfrac{-56}{-8}$
(5)   (5)

Select the correct mathematical expression for each of the following phrases.

11. the sum of 3 and 6, all multiplied by -9
(2)
    A. $3 \cdot 6 + (-9)$ B. $3 + 6(-9)$ C. $-9(3) + 6$
    D. $3(6 + -9)$ E. $-9(3 + 6)$

12.
(2) the quotient of −15 and 5 decreased by 8

    A. $8 - \dfrac{-15}{5}$ B. $\dfrac{-15}{5} - 8$ C. $\dfrac{5}{-15} - 8$

    D. $\dfrac{-15}{8-5}$ E. $\dfrac{-15}{5-8}$

Select an equation to represent each problem below.

13.
(2) The sum of some number and 12 is divided by 3, and the result is equal to 20.

    A. $\dfrac{x+12}{3} = 20$ B. $\dfrac{x}{12+3} = 20$ C. $\dfrac{x}{3} + 12 = 20$

    D. $x + \dfrac{12}{3} = 20$ E. $\dfrac{3}{x+12} = 20$

14.
(2) The product of some number and 4 is decreased by 7, and the result is 18.

    A. $4 \cdot 7 \cdot x = 18$ B. $7(x-4) = 18$ C. $\dfrac{4x}{7} = 18$

    D. $4x - 7 = 18$ E. $7 - 4x = 18$

State whether each pair of fractions below have the same value.

15.
(6) $\dfrac{2}{-5}$ and $-\dfrac{2}{5}$ **16.**
(6) $\dfrac{-3}{-11}$ and $-\dfrac{3}{11}$

Solve each equation below by undoing.

17.
(6) $x - (-7) = 29$ **18.**
(3) $5x + 11 = 46$ **19.**
(3) $\dfrac{x-4}{2} = \dfrac{5}{2}$

20.
(6) $\dfrac{-x}{6} + 1 = 18$ **21.**
(3) $3(x-12) = 51$ **22.**
(6) $\dfrac{1}{2}x - 1 = -\dfrac{1}{3}$

23.
(6) $-3.2 - x = -19.4$ **24.**
(3) $\dfrac{1}{2}\left(x + \dfrac{2}{3}\right) = \dfrac{5}{4}$

Translate the word problem below into an equation; then solve.

25. Because of inflation, Frank's Frankfurters Incorporated increased the price of their
(4) award-winning hot dogs by $2. But when sales nose-dived, the company was forced to
cut the new price in half to sell all the extra hot dogs they had in stock. If the final price
of the hot dogs was $2.50, what was the original price?

Chapter 2 Test

Tell whether each sentence below is True or False.

1.
(7) Simplify means to rewrite an expression in a simpler form without changing its value.

2.
(12) When distributing to free an x from more than one set of parentheses, you distribute over the innermost set first.

Complete each sentence below with the best of the choices given.

3.
(7) The _____ states that the order in which two numbers are multiplied won't affect the answer.

    A. commutative property of addition
    B. commutative property of multiplication
    C. associative property of addition
    D. associative property of multiplication
    E. distributive property

4.
(7) In letters, the associative property of addition is shown by the statement _____.

    A. $a+b=b+a$ B. $ab=ba$ C. $(a+b)+c=a+(b+c)$

    D. $a(b+c)=ab+ac$ E. none of the above

Calculate the value of each expression below.

5.
(5) $\dfrac{5+(-9)}{-2}$

6.
(5) $-(2+7)-3(-5)$

7.
(12) $3[1+5(4-2)]$

Tell whether each pair of expressions below is equivalent.

8.
(13) $\dfrac{x-7}{3}$ and $\dfrac{1}{3}x-\dfrac{7}{3}$

9.
(12) $3x+4[2(x+1)+5]$ and $11x+28$

Select the simplified form of each expression below.

10.
(9) $5.1x+(-2.7x)$

    A. $-13.77x$ B. $1.9x$ C. $7.8x$
    D. $-2.4x$ E. $2.4x$

11.
(8)
$-6+8x+9$

A. $2x+9$ B. $8x+3$ C. $-6+17x$
D. $8x+(-3)$ E. $11x$

12.
(13)
$y-\dfrac{2y}{5}$

A. $-\dfrac{3}{5}y$ B. $-\dfrac{2}{5}y$ C. $\dfrac{3}{5}y$

D. $-\dfrac{1}{5}y$ E. $\dfrac{7}{5}y$

13.
(7)
$\dfrac{4}{5}(x+10)$

A. $\dfrac{4}{5}x+8$ B. $\dfrac{4}{5}x+\dfrac{2}{25}$ C. $\dfrac{4}{5}x+10$

D. $\dfrac{4}{5}x+\dfrac{14}{5}$ E. $x+10\dfrac{4}{5}$

14.
(10)
$3(x-6)-7(x+1)$

A. $2x-9$ B. $-29x$ C. $-4x+(-5)$
D. $-4x+(-25)$ E. $-4x+(-11)$

15.
(12)
$5[2(x-4)]$

A. $7x-4$ B. $10x-40$ C. $10x-20$
D. $10x-4$ E. $7x-28$

Solve each equation below. Indicate any false equations or identities.

16.
(8)
$2.8+2x+0.9=17.7$

17.
(9)
$\dfrac{1}{4}x+\dfrac{1}{2}x=12$

18.
(14)
$8x+5=3x-7$

19.
(10)
$9x+4(x-3)=14$

20.
(13)
$\dfrac{y}{2}+y=-1$

21.
(14)
$7(x-3)=-21+7x$

22.
(13)
$2x+\dfrac{x-6}{2}=0$

23.
(14)
$5x\cdot 2=10x+3$

24.
(12)
$4x+2[3(x-1)+2]=8$

Translate the word problem below into an equation; then solve.

25. Mr. Cash invested $80,000 in various stocks and bonds. He earned a 7% dividend on his
(11) stocks and 5% interest on his bonds, for a one year profit (from both stocks and bonds) of
$4,900. How much did Mr. Cash invest in bonds?

Chapter 3 Test

Tell whether each sentence below is True or False.

1.
(16)
When a fraction has an x in its denominator, that x can't have a value that will make the denominator equal zero.

2.
(18)
When multiplying fractions with x's, it's easier to factor and cancel after multiplying.

3.
(21)
To clear more than one fraction from an equation, you multiply both sides by the lowest common denominator of the fractions.

Calculate the value of each expression below.

4.
(5)
$8(-2)-(-5)(6)$

5.
(12)
$-5[10-3(7+4)]$

6.
(5)
$\dfrac{9-21}{-7+3}$

Select the simplified form of each expression below.

7.
(17)
$\dfrac{8x+4}{6x+3}$

   A. $2x+1$ B. $\dfrac{4x+4}{3}$ C. 4

   D. $\dfrac{3}{4}$ E. $\dfrac{4}{3}$

8.
(18)
$\dfrac{5x}{4} \cdot \dfrac{12}{25x}$

   A. $\dfrac{17}{29}$ B. $\dfrac{1}{15}$ C. $\dfrac{2x}{5}$

   D. $\dfrac{5x+12}{4+25x}$ E. $\dfrac{3}{5}$

9.
(18)
$\dfrac{x-4}{18x} \div \dfrac{2x-8}{9}$

   A. $\dfrac{1}{4x}$ B. $\dfrac{1}{x}$ C. $\dfrac{x-4}{9x}$

   D. $\dfrac{1}{18x}$ E. $\dfrac{-x+4}{9x}$

10.
(19)
$\dfrac{x+5}{2x} - \dfrac{3x+2}{x}$

   A. $\dfrac{-5x+9}{2x}$ B. $\dfrac{-2x+3}{2x}$ C. $\dfrac{-5x+1}{2x}$

   D. $\dfrac{-5x+3}{2x}$ E. $-\dfrac{2x-3}{x}$

11.
(12)
$3[-4(x+2)+1]$

   A. $-12x+9$ B. $-12x+27$ C. $-12x+(-23)$

   D. $-x$ E. $-12x+(-21)$

12.
(19)
$\dfrac{5x}{2x+6} + \dfrac{x-3}{x+3}$

   A. $\dfrac{11x-3}{2x+6}$ B. $\dfrac{7x+6}{2x+6}$ C. $\dfrac{2x-1}{x+3}$

   D. $\dfrac{7x-6}{2x+6}$ E. $\dfrac{7x-3}{2x+6}$

Tell whether each pair of expressions below is equivalent.

13.
(17)
$\dfrac{3x+19}{3x}$ and 19 **14.**
(13)
$-\dfrac{y}{2} - 3y$ and $-5y$

Solve each equation below. Indicate any false equations or identities. Make sure your answer is fully reduced.

15.
(20)
$\dfrac{5}{9x} = 1$ **16.**
(20)
$\dfrac{1}{x-7} = -8$ **17.**
(14)
$24 - 3x = -6x + 22$

18.
(12)
$3[4(x-2)+x] = 21$ **19.**
(13)
$\dfrac{2x+10}{2} = -43$ **20.**
(21)
$\dfrac{5}{3x+6} = \dfrac{2}{9x}$

21.
(14)
$8x + 11 - x = 7x$ **22.**
(21)
$\dfrac{2x}{3} + \dfrac{x}{2} = \dfrac{5}{6}$ **23.**
(21)
$\dfrac{4}{5x+15} - \dfrac{1}{x+3} = \dfrac{3}{5}$

Translate the word problem below into an equation; then solve.

24.
(3)
Margaret went to the convenience store and purchased 4 cans of cola for $2.76. How many cans could she have purchased (at the same price) for $13.11?

Chapter 4 Test

Tell whether each sentence below is True or False.

1. A power is a shortcut for writing a repeated multiplication.
(22)

2. Terms with x's raised to the same power are called like terms.
(23)

3. The shortcut for multiplying powers is to add their exponents.
(24)

Calculate the value of each expression below.

4. $5 \cdot 3^2 - 7$
(22)

5. $\dfrac{4^2 - 2^3}{-2}$
(22)

6. $-3(2+5)^2$
(22)

Rewrite each number below in scientific notation.

7. 5,400,000,000
(29)

8. 0.000000027
(29)

Calculate the value of each expression below. Leave your answers in scientific notation.

9. $(3.2 \times 10^7)(5.6 \times 10^4)$
(29)

10. $\dfrac{(1.2 \times 10^9)(4.4 \times 10^8)}{3.0 \times 10^{21}}$
(29)

Tell whether each of the following pairs of expressions is equivalent.

11. $3x^{-6}$ and $\dfrac{3}{x^6}$
(26)

12. $-2x^5 + 3x^4 + 9x^5 - 8x^4$ and $7x^5 - 5x^4$
(23)

Select the simplified form of each expression below.

13. $(6x^8)(9x^7)$
(24)

    A. $3x$ B. $54x^{15}$ C. $15x^{56}$

    D. $54x^{56}$ E. $15x^{15}$

14.
(27)
$$\dfrac{y^2 + 8y + 15}{y^2 + 7y + 10}$$

    A. $\dfrac{y+3}{y+2}$ B. $y+5$ C. $\dfrac{y+2}{y+3}$

    D. $\dfrac{y+1}{y+2}$ E. $\dfrac{y+5}{y+2}$

15.
(25)
$(x+5)(x^2 + 3x + 2)$

    A. $x^3 + 3x + 10$ B. $x^2 + 4x + 7$ C. $5x^3 + 15x^2 + 10x$

    D. $x^3 + 8x^2 + 17x + 10$ E. $x^3 + 15x^2 + 30x + 10$

16.
(28)
$$\dfrac{x^2 - 6x + 5}{3x^2} \div \dfrac{2x - 10}{9x}$$

    A. $\dfrac{x^2 - 4x - 5}{3x^2 + 9x}$ B. $\dfrac{3x - 3}{2x}$ C. $\dfrac{3x - 3}{2}$

    D. $\dfrac{x + 8}{2x}$ E. $\dfrac{3x - 1}{2x}$

17.
(28)
$$\dfrac{5}{x+3} + \dfrac{2x}{x^2 + 6x + 9}$$

    A. $\dfrac{2x + 5}{x^2 + 7x + 12}$ B. $\dfrac{2x^2 + 6x + 5}{x^2 + 6x + 9}$ C. $\dfrac{7x + 3}{x^2 + 6x + 9}$

    D. $\dfrac{10x}{x^2 + 6x + 9}$ E. $\dfrac{7x + 15}{x^2 + 6x + 9}$

18.
(28)
$$\dfrac{z^3 + 1}{2z^2 + 4z} - \dfrac{3z^2}{z + 2}$$

    A. $\dfrac{-3z^4 - 3z}{2z + 4}$ B. $\dfrac{-4z^3 + 1}{2z^2 + 4z}$ C. $\dfrac{z^3 - 3z^2 + 1}{2z^2 + 3z - 2}$

    D. $\dfrac{-5z^3 + 1}{2z^2 + 4z}$ E. $\dfrac{7z^3 + 1}{2z^2 + 4z}$

Solve each equation below.

19.
(14)
$-4.2x + 3 = -9 + 1.8x$ **20.**
(21)
$\dfrac{3x}{2} = \dfrac{x}{2} + 4$ **21.**
(14)
$-3(x + 7) = 2(x - 1)$

22. $\dfrac{2}{5x} + \dfrac{x+1}{x} = 2$
(21)

23. $3[x + 2(x+4)] = 60$
(12)

24. $\dfrac{4x}{3x-12} = \dfrac{1}{x-4}$
(21)

Translate the word problem below into an equation; then solve.

25. Mr. Pyle, the gasoline station attendant, mixed \$1.95 per gallon unleaded gas with 65
(11) gallons of \$2.15 per gallon premium gas to create a \$2.00 gas blend called *Budget Premium*. How many gallons of the unleaded gas did Mr. Pyle use?

Chapter 5 Test

Tell whether each sentence below is True or False.

1.
(30) The inverse of raising a number to a power is taking a root.

2.
(32) To multiply irrationals, multiply the numbers under the radical signs and take the root of the result.

Rewrite each number below in regular decimal form.

3. 1.48×10^7
(29)

4. 7.6×10^{-4}
(29)

Tell whether each number below is rational or irrational.

5. $\sqrt[3]{4}$
(31)

6. $\sqrt{81}$
(31)

Give a decimal estimate to two places (hundredths) for each irrational number below.

7. $\sqrt{13}$
(31)

8. $\sqrt{17}$
(31)

Change each root below into a power.

9. $\sqrt{5}$
(37)

10. $\sqrt[5]{3^2}$
(37)

Answer each question below.

11. Select the simplified form of the expression $\sqrt{11} \cdot \sqrt{2}$.
(32)

  A. 22   B. 3   C. $\sqrt{13}$

  D. $\sqrt{22}$ E. $2\sqrt{11}$

12. Select the simplified form of the expression $7\sqrt{3}+\sqrt{12}$.
(34)

   A. $7\sqrt{15}$ B. $14\sqrt{3}$ C. 42

   D. $11\sqrt{3}$ E. $9\sqrt{3}$

13. Select the simplified form of the expression $\dfrac{\sqrt[3]{20}}{\sqrt[3]{5}}$.
(32)

   A. $\sqrt[3]{4}$ B. $\sqrt[3]{15}$ C. $\dfrac{1}{\sqrt[3]{4}}$

   D. $\sqrt[3]{25}$ E. $\sqrt[3]{100}$

14. Multiply $\sqrt[3]{7}\cdot\sqrt{7}$ using fractional exponents.
(37)

   A. $7^{\frac{1}{2}}$ B. $7^{\frac{5}{6}}$ C. $7^{\frac{1}{6}}$

   D. $7^{\frac{2}{3}}$ E. $7^{\frac{6}{5}}$

15. Divide $\dfrac{\sqrt{2}}{\sqrt[5]{2}}$ using fractional exponents.
(37)

   A. $2^{\frac{5}{2}}$ B. $2^{\frac{10}{3}}$ C. $2^{\frac{3}{10}}$

   D. $2^{\frac{2}{5}}$ E. $2^{\frac{1}{10}}$

16. Simplify $\dfrac{\sqrt{5}}{\sqrt{7}}$ by rationalizing the denominator and select your answer from the choices
(36)

below.

   A. $\dfrac{\sqrt{2}}{7}$ B. $\dfrac{5}{\sqrt{35}}$ C. $\dfrac{2\sqrt{3}}{7}$

   D. $\dfrac{\sqrt{35}}{7}$ E. $\dfrac{1}{\sqrt{2}}$

Select the factored form of each expression below.

17. $21y^3+14y^2$
(27)

   A. $14y^2(7y+1)$ B. $21y^2(y+7)$ C. $7y^3(3+2y)$

   D. $7y(3y^2+2)$ E. $7y^2(3y+2)$

18. $x^2 - 9x + 20$
(27)

    A. $(x-5)(x-4)$ B. $(x+5)(x+4)$ C. $(x-10)(x+2)$

    D. $(x-20)(x-1)$ E. $(x-20)(x+1)$

Select the simplified form of each expression below.

19. $(3^2 x^4)^{-3}$
(26)

    A. $\dfrac{x}{243}$ B. $\dfrac{1}{729x^{12}}$ C. $\dfrac{1}{3x}$

    D. $-729x^{12}$ E. $\dfrac{1}{3x^{12}}$

20. $\dfrac{x^2 - 2x - 8}{3x^2 + 9x} \cdot \dfrac{3x - 18}{x + 2}$
(28)

    A. $\dfrac{2x-10}{x^2+3x}$ B. $\dfrac{x^2-10x+24}{x^2+3x}$ C. $\dfrac{x-4}{x^2+3x}$

    D. $\dfrac{x-4}{x+3}$ E. $\dfrac{x^2+x-26}{3x^2+10x+2}$

21. $\dfrac{3y}{y^2 + 3y - 10} - \dfrac{5}{2y + 10}$
(28)

    A. $\dfrac{5y-5}{y^2+3y-10}$ B. $\dfrac{3y-5}{y^2+y-20}$ C. $\dfrac{y+10}{2y^2+6y-20}$

    D. $\dfrac{y-10}{2y^2+6y-20}$ E. $\dfrac{-y+5}{y^2+3y-10}$

Solve each equation below.

22. $7y - (9 + 4y) = -3$
(10)

23. $\dfrac{2z-1}{3} - \dfrac{3z+1}{5} = 1$
(21)

24. $\dfrac{7}{3x+1} = \dfrac{2}{x+2}$
(21)

Translate the word problem below into an equation; then solve.

25. Truck #1 and Truck #2 left from the same location at the same time, driving in opposite
(15) directions. If Truck #1 traveled at 70 mph and Truck #2 at 65 mph, how many hours was
it before they were 1,755 miles apart?

Chapter 6 Test

Tell whether each sentence below is True or False.

1. Second-degree equations can never have two solutions.
(38)

2. The quadratic formula can be used to solve second-degree equations that are too hard to factor.
(43)

Calculate the value of each expression below. Leave your answer in scientific notation.

3. $(4.2 \times 10^9)(3.2 \times 10^{-13})$
(29)

4. $\dfrac{2.1 \times 10^{10}}{7 \times 10^{17}}$
(29)

Answer each question below.

5. Simplify the expression $(\sqrt{5} + 2)(\sqrt{5} - 9)$ by multiplying and select your answer from the choices below.
(35)

    A. $7\sqrt{5} + (-13)$ B. $-7\sqrt{5} + (-13)$ C. $-18\sqrt{5} + (-13)$

    D. -13 E. $-7\sqrt{5} + (-23)$

6. Simplify the expression $\dfrac{\sqrt{2}}{\sqrt{3} - \sqrt{7}}$ by rationalizing the denominator and select your answer from the choices below.
(36)

    A. $-\dfrac{\sqrt{6} + \sqrt{14}}{2}$ B. $\dfrac{2}{\sqrt{6} - \sqrt{14}}$ C. $-\dfrac{\sqrt{5} + \sqrt{10}}{4}$

    D. $-\dfrac{\sqrt{6} + \sqrt{14}}{10}$ E. $-\dfrac{\sqrt{6} + \sqrt{14}}{4}$

7. Simplify the expression $\dfrac{11^{\frac{4}{5}}}{11^{\frac{1}{5}}}$ by dividing and select your answer from the choices below.
(37)

    A. $11^{\frac{3}{5}}$ B. 11^4 C. 11

    D. $11^{\frac{1}{4}}$ E. $11^{\frac{5}{3}}$

Select the factored form of each expression below.

8. $x^2 - 5x - 36$
(27)

    A. $(x+12)(x-3)$ B. $(x-9)(x-4)$ C. $(x+9)(x-4)$

    D. $(x-9)(x+4)$ E. $(x-12)(x+3)$

9. $2x^2 + 7x + 5$
(41)

    A. $(2x+5)(2x+1)$ B. $(2x-1)(x-5)$ C. $(2x+5)(x+1)$

    D. $(2x+1)(x+5)$ E. $(2x-5)(x-1)$

Select the simplified form of each expression below.

10. $\dfrac{(3x^{-4})^3}{5x^2}$
(26)

    A. $\dfrac{27}{5x^{14}}$ B. $-\dfrac{9x^5}{5}$ C. $\dfrac{9}{5x^3}$

    D. $\dfrac{9}{5x^{14}}$ E. $\dfrac{27}{5x}$

11. $\dfrac{\frac{y+2}{4y^2}}{\frac{3y+6}{2y^3}}$
(28)

    A. $\dfrac{y^2+2y}{3}$ B. $\dfrac{3y^2+12y+12}{8y^5}$ C. $\dfrac{y}{3}$

    D. $\dfrac{y}{6}$ E. $\dfrac{2y+4}{y^3+2y^2}$

12. $\dfrac{x}{x-4} + \dfrac{2}{x^2-4x}$
(28)

    A. $\dfrac{x+2}{x^2-3x-4}$ B. $\dfrac{x^2+2}{x^2-4x}$ C. $\dfrac{x+2}{x^2-4x}$

    D. $\dfrac{3}{x-4}$ E. $\dfrac{x^2-8}{x^2-4x}$

Tell whether each of the following pairs of expressions is equivalent.

13.
(23)
$\frac{1}{3}x^2 + \frac{x^2}{4}$ and $\frac{7}{12}x^2$

14.
(25)
$(x+4)(x+5)(x+1)$ and $3x+10$

Solve each equation below. Be sure to give *every* solution.

15.
(3)
$\frac{3x-5}{7} = 0$

16.
(39)
$(x+5)^2 - 18 = 63$

Solve the equation below and select the choice that contains *all* of the solutions.

17.
(39)
$2x^2 - 3 = 19$

    A. $+2\sqrt{11}, \ -2\sqrt{11}$ B. $+4\sqrt{2}, \ -4\sqrt{2}$ C. $+22, \ -22$

    D. $+\sqrt{11}, \ -\sqrt{11}$ E. $+2\sqrt{2}, \ -2\sqrt{2}$

Solve each equation below by factoring. Be sure to give *every* solution.

18.
(40)
$2x^2 + 8x = 0$

19.
(40)
$x^2 - 10x = -21$

20.
(41)
$2x^2 - 3x = 5$

Solve the equation below by completing the square and select the choice that contains *all* of the solutions.

21.
(42)
$x^2 + 4x - 1 = 0$

    A. $+\sqrt{2}-5, \ -\sqrt{2}-5$ B. $+\sqrt{5}+2, \ -\sqrt{5}+2$ C. $+2\sqrt{5}, \ -2\sqrt{5}$

    D. $-3, \ -1$ E. $+\sqrt{5}-2, \ -\sqrt{5}-2$

Solve each equation below using the quadratic formula, $x = \dfrac{-b \pm \sqrt{b^2 - 4ac}}{2a}$, and select the choice that contains *all* of the solutions.

22.
(43)
$2x^2 + 5x - 1 = 0$

    A. $\dfrac{-5+\sqrt{33}}{4}, \ \dfrac{-5-\sqrt{33}}{4}$ B. $\dfrac{-5+3\sqrt{3}}{4}, \ \dfrac{-5-3\sqrt{3}}{4}$ C. $\dfrac{5+\sqrt{17}}{2}, \ \dfrac{5-\sqrt{17}}{2}$

    D. $\dfrac{-5+\sqrt{33}}{2}, \ \dfrac{-5-\sqrt{33}}{2}$ E. $\dfrac{-5+\sqrt{17}}{4}, \ \dfrac{-5-\sqrt{17}}{4}$

23. $3x^2 + 7x = 1$
(43)

    A. $\dfrac{-7+\sqrt{52}}{6}, \dfrac{-7-\sqrt{52}}{6}$ B. $\dfrac{-7+\sqrt{37}}{6}, \dfrac{-7-\sqrt{37}}{6}$ C. $\dfrac{7+\sqrt{46}}{3}, \dfrac{7-\sqrt{46}}{3}$

    D. $\dfrac{-7+\sqrt{61}}{6}, \dfrac{-7-\sqrt{61}}{6}$ E. $\dfrac{-7+\sqrt{61}}{3}, \dfrac{-7-\sqrt{61}}{3}$

Translate the word problem below into an equation; then solve.

24. One positive integer is 5 times another positive integer and their product is 320. What are
(39)   the positive integers?

Chapter 7 Test

Tell whether each sentence below is True or False.

1. Equations with an x under a radical sign are called radical equations.
(44)

2. It is always necessary to check the solutions to a radical equation.
(44)

Find the values for *a*, *b*, and *c* for each quadratic equation below.

3. $4x^2 + 2x - 1 = 0$
(43)

4. $3x^2 - 5x = 11$
(43)

Answer each question below.

5. Simplify the expression $3\sqrt{12} + 2\sqrt{3}$ by combining and select your answer from the
(34) choices below.

    A. $5\sqrt{15}$ B. $8\sqrt{3}$ C. $12\sqrt{3}$

    D. $7\sqrt{3}$ E. 36

6. Divide $\dfrac{\sqrt{35}}{\sqrt{5}}$.
(32)

7. Multiply $\sqrt[4]{5} \cdot \sqrt[3]{5}$ using fractional exponents.
(37)

Select the factored form of each expression below.

8. $18x^3 + 9x^2$
(27)

    A. $18x^3(1 + 9x)$ B. $9x^3(2 + x)$ C. $9x^2(9x + 1)$

    D. $9x^3(9 + x)$ E. $9x^2(2x + 1)$

9. $x^2 - 8x - 20$
(27)

    A. $(x - 10)(x + 2)$ B. $(x + 5)(x - 4)$ C. $(x + 10)(x - 2)$

    D. $(x - 20)(x + 1)$ E. $(x - 5)(x + 4)$

10. $2x^2 - 5x + 3$
(41)

    A. $(2x+3)(x+1)$ B. $(2x+1)(2x-3)$ C. $(2x-3)(x-1)$

    D. $(2x+1)(x+3)$ E. $(2x-1)(x-3)$

Select the simplified form of each expression below.

11. $(5z^2)(4z^{-6})$
(26)

    A. $\dfrac{20}{z^4}$ B. $\dfrac{9}{z^4}$ C. $\dfrac{9}{z^{12}}$

    D. $-20z^4$ E. $20z^4$

12. $\dfrac{x-2}{3x^3} \cdot \dfrac{9x^2}{x^2-4x+4}$
(28)

    A. $\dfrac{3}{x}$ B. $\dfrac{3x-6}{x}$ C. $\dfrac{3}{x^2-2x}$

    D. $\dfrac{9x^2+x-2}{3x^3+x^2-4x+4}$ E. $\dfrac{3}{x-2}$

13. $\dfrac{5}{x-3} - \dfrac{2x+4}{x^2-4x+3}$
(28)

    A. $\dfrac{3}{x-1}$ B. $\dfrac{-2x+1}{-x^2+5x-6}$ C. $\dfrac{3x-5}{x^2-4x+3}$

    D. $\dfrac{3}{x-3}$ E. $\dfrac{3x-1}{x^2-4x-3}$

Tell whether each pair of expressions below is equivalent.

14. $\dfrac{6x-15x^3}{-10x^3+4x}$ and $\dfrac{3}{2}$ **15.** $8x^2+18x-5$ and $(4x-1)(2x+5)$
(27)   (41)

Solve each equation below. Be sure to list only valid solutions. If an equation has no valid solutions just write "No solution."

16. $\dfrac{1}{2x} - \dfrac{3}{5x} = 1$ **17.** $2\sqrt{x}-4=10$ **18.** $\sqrt{5x-1}=2$
(21)   (44)   (45)

19. $\sqrt{x-2} = x-4$ **20.** $\sqrt{x+9} - \sqrt{2x-7} = 0$
(46)   (47)

Solve the equation below and select the choice that contains *all* of the solutions.

21. $\dfrac{1}{\sqrt{x+3}} = \sqrt{-2x}$
(48)

A. $-\dfrac{3+\sqrt{7}}{2}, \ -\dfrac{3-\sqrt{7}}{2}$ B. $0, \ -3$ C. $\dfrac{-3+\sqrt{11}}{2}, \ \dfrac{-3-\sqrt{11}}{2}$

D. $\dfrac{-6+\sqrt{7}}{4}, \ \dfrac{-6-\sqrt{7}}{4}$ E. 2

Solve the equation below. Be sure to give *every* solution.

22. $y^2 + 2y = 35$
(43)

Solve the equation below by using the quadratic formula, $x = \dfrac{-b \pm \sqrt{b^2 - 4ac}}{2a}$, and select the choice that contains *all* of the solutions.

23. $2x^2 + 5x - 5 = 0$
(43)

A. $\dfrac{5+\sqrt{65}}{2}, \ \dfrac{5-\sqrt{65}}{2}$ B. $\dfrac{-5+\sqrt{35}}{2}, \ \dfrac{-5-\sqrt{35}}{2}$ C. $\dfrac{-5+\sqrt{15}}{4}, \ \dfrac{-5-\sqrt{15}}{4}$

D. $\dfrac{-5+\sqrt{65}}{4}, \ \dfrac{-5-\sqrt{65}}{4}$ E. $\dfrac{-5+5\sqrt{2}}{4}, \ \dfrac{-5-5\sqrt{2}}{4}$

Translate the word problem below into an equation; then solve.

24. Benny the carhop has 2 times as many dimes as quarters. If Benny has $41.85 worth of
(9)   dimes and quarters combined, how many quarters does he have?

78

Chapter 8 Test

Tell whether each sentence below is True or False.

1. Imaginary numbers are used to allow numbers to represent not two, but four directions.
(50)

2. Complex numbers make it possible to represent more than four directions.
(50)

Use the discriminant to tell whether the solutions of each equation below are real or complex.

3. $x^2 + 5x + 2 = 0$ **4.** $4x^2 - 3x + 9 = 0$
(56)   (56)

Rewrite each imaginary number below using i and then select your answer from the choices. Make sure the answer is fully simplified.

5. $\sqrt{-81}$
(49)

     A. $-9\sqrt{i}$ B. $81i$ C. $-81i$

     D. $-9i$ E. $9i$

6. $\sqrt{-20}$
(49)

     A. $2\sqrt{5}i$ B. $-20\sqrt{i}$ C. $4\sqrt{5}i$

     D. $-2\sqrt{5}i$ E. $4\sqrt{5}\cdot i$

Select a complex number to represent each quantity below.

7. the quantity 4 units to the north
(53)

     A. $-4+i$ B. $-4i$ C. $4+i$

     D. $4i$ E. $4-i$

8. the quantity $\sqrt{11}$ units to the south
(53)

     A. $-11i$ B. $\sqrt{11}-i$ C. $-\sqrt{11}i$

     D. $\sqrt{11}+i$ E. $\sqrt{11}i$

Calculate the value of each expression below and then select your answer from the choices. Make sure the answer is fully simplified.

9.
(54)
$(1+4i)+(9+8i)$

    A. $10+12i$ B. $10+32i$ C. 41
    D. $9+32i$ E. -23

10.
(52)
$\sqrt{2}i \cdot \sqrt{6}i$

    A. $-2\sqrt{2}$ B. $2\sqrt{2}+2i$ C. $2\sqrt{3}$
    D. $2\sqrt{2}$ E. $-2\sqrt{3}$

11.
(54)
$(7+5i)-[(-2+(-3i)]$

    A. 1   B. $9+8i$ C. $-14+2i$
    D. $5+2i$ E. $-14-15i$

12.
(52)
$-23i^6$

    A. $-23i$ B. $23i$ C. 23
    D. $-138i$ E. -23

13.
(52)
$(5+2i)(1+3i)$

    A. $-1+17i$ B. $11+17i$ C. 5
    D. $5+5i$ E. $6+5i$

14.
(52)
$\dfrac{11i}{\sqrt{2}i}$

    A. $\dfrac{11\sqrt{2}}{2}$ B. $\dfrac{11+\sqrt{2}}{2}i$ C. $11\sqrt{2}$

    D. $\dfrac{11\sqrt{2}i}{2}$ E. $11\sqrt{2}i$

15.
(52)
$(2i)^5$

    A. 32   B. $-32i$ C. -32
    D. $10i$ E. $32i$

Select the simplified form of each expression below.

16.
(26)
$(5y^7)^{-3}$

    A. $\dfrac{y^4}{125}$ B. $\dfrac{1}{125y^{21}}$ C. $-125y^4$

    D. $\dfrac{1}{15y^4}$ E. $\dfrac{-15}{y^{21}}$

17.
(27)
$\dfrac{y^2 - 10y + 25}{3y - 15}$

    A. $\dfrac{3}{y-5}$ B. $3y - 15$ C. $\dfrac{y-5}{3}$

    D. $\dfrac{1}{3y-15}$ E. $y - 5$

18.
(19)
$\dfrac{x+2}{2x-2} + \dfrac{4x-3}{10x-10}$

    A. $\dfrac{21x-13}{10x-10}$ B. $\dfrac{5x-1}{12x-12}$ C. $\dfrac{9x-1}{10x-10}$

    D. $\dfrac{9x+7}{10x-10}$ E. $\dfrac{9x+15}{10x-10}$

Solve each equation below. Be sure to list only valid solutions. If an equation has no valid solutions just write "No solution."

19.
(40)
$5x - 10x^2 = 0$

20.
(45)
$\dfrac{\sqrt{2x}+7}{4} = 3$

21.
(46)
$\sqrt{x^2+11} = 6$

Solve each equation below and select the choice that contains *all* of the solutions.

22.
(49)
$x^2 = -29$

    A. $+\sqrt{29},\ -\sqrt{29}$ B. $+\sqrt{29}-i,\ -\sqrt{29}-i$ C. $+\sqrt{29}i,\ -\sqrt{29}i$

    D. $+29-i,\ -29-i$ E. $+29-\sqrt{i},\ -29-\sqrt{i}$

23. $(x+6)^2 = -9$
(55)

   A. $+3\sqrt{i}, \ -3\sqrt{i}$ B. $-6+3\sqrt{i}, \ -6-3\sqrt{i}$ C. $-6+\sqrt{3i}, \ -6-\sqrt{3i}$

   D. $-\sqrt{6}+3i, \ -\sqrt{6}-3i$ E. $-6+3i, \ -6-3i$

Solve the equation below by using the quadratic formula, $x = \dfrac{-b \pm \sqrt{b^2 - 4ac}}{2a}$, and select the choice that contains *all* of the solutions.

24. $x^2 + 3x + 8 = 0$
(43)

   A. $3+\sqrt{23}i, \ 3-\sqrt{23}i$ B. $\dfrac{-3+\sqrt{17}i}{2}, \dfrac{-3-\sqrt{17}i}{2}$ C. $\dfrac{-3+\sqrt{23}i}{2}, \dfrac{-3-\sqrt{23}i}{2}$

   D. $\dfrac{-3+\sqrt{41}i}{2}, \dfrac{-3-\sqrt{41}i}{2}$ E. $\dfrac{-3i+\sqrt{23}i}{2}, \dfrac{-3i-\sqrt{23}i}{2}$

Translate the word problem below into an equation; then solve.

25. The second angle of a triangle is twice the first, while the third angle of the triangle is 1.5
(9)   times the second. What is the measure of the first angle? Remember, the sum of the angles in any triangle is 180 degrees.

Chapter 9 Test

Tell whether each sentence below is True or False.

1. A polynomial is an expression with x's that have only whole number exponents.
(59)

2. Polynomial division is an algebra version of long division.
(59)

Give a decimal estimate to two places (hundredths) for each irrational number below. Be sure to get a decimal estimate for the square root (using a calculator) before doing anything else.

3. $3 + \sqrt{14}$
(31)

4. $\dfrac{-2 - \sqrt{51}}{3}$
(31)

Use the discriminant to tell whether the solutions of each equation below are real or complex.

5. $3x^2 - 2x + 1 = 0$
(56)

6. $x^2 - 7x + 3 = 0$
(56)

7. $-2x^2 + 5x - 4 = 0$
(56)

Calculate the value of each expression below and then select your answer from the choices. Make sure the answer is fully simplified.

8. $(-4 + 7i) + (-2 + 5i)$
(54)

    A. $-6 + 12i$ B. $-6 + 2i$ C. $8 + 35i$

    D. -27 E. $-2 + 12i$

9. $(-3i^4)^3$
(52)

    A. $27i$ B. $-9i$ C. 9

    D. 27 E. -27

10. $(-3 + i)(8 + 2i)$
(52)

    A. $-26 + 2i$ B. $-22 + 14i$ C. $5 + 3i$

    D. $-26 + 14i$ E. -26

Select the factored form of each expression below.

11. $x^2 - 4x + 3$
(27)

    A. $(x+3)(x+1)$ B. $(x-2)(x-1)$ C. $(x+4)(x-3)$

    D. $(x+3)(x-4)$ E. $(x-3)(x-1)$

12. $2x^2 - 13x - 7$
(41)

    A. $(2x+7)(x-1)$ B. $(2x-7)(x-1)$ C. $(2x-7)(x+1)$

    D. $(2x+1)(x-7)$ E. $(2x-7)(2x-1)$

13. $x^3 + 7x^2 + 12x$
(57)

    A. $(x^2+6)(x+2)$ B. $x(x+4)(x+3)$ C. $x(x+12)(x+1)$

    D. $x(x+6)(x+2)$ E. $(x^2+4)(x+3)$

Select the simplified form of each expression below.

14. $-11x^5 + (7x^5)$
(23)

    A. $-4x^{25}$ B. $18x^{10}$ C. $4x^5$

    D. $-4x^{10}$ E. $-4x^5$

15. $\dfrac{6y}{10y^3} \div \dfrac{18y^2}{5y^3}$
(28)

    A. $\dfrac{1}{6y}$ B. $\dfrac{54}{5y^3}$ C. $\dfrac{8}{5y^3}$

    D. $\dfrac{y^2}{5}$ E. $\dfrac{1}{6y^2}$

16. $2x^2(x^3 - 8x)$
(25)

    A. $2x^5 - 10x^3$ B. $2x^5 - 16x^3$ C. $2x^5 - 6x^3$

    D. $2x^6 - 16x^2$ E. $-16x^6$

17.
(28)
$$\frac{5-2x}{4x+12x^2}-\frac{5-6x}{4x+12x^2}$$

A. $\dfrac{5-4x}{2x+6x^2}$ B. $\dfrac{-2}{1+3x}$ C. $\dfrac{4}{1+3x}$

D. $\dfrac{1}{1+3x}$ E. $\dfrac{-4x}{1+3x}$

18.
(60)
$$\frac{2x^3+11x^2+13x+4}{x+4}$$

A. $2x^2+19x+89$ B. x^2+5x+3 C. $2x^2+1$

D. $2x^2+7x+9$ E. $2x^2+3x+1$

Solve each equation below. Be sure to list only valid solutions. If an equation has no valid solutions just write "No solution."

19.
(14)
$\dfrac{9-3x}{2}=5x$

20.
(57)
$x^3+4x^2+3x=0$

21.
(47)
$\sqrt{8x-9}=\sqrt{15+7x}$

22.
(61)
$x^3-2x^2-x+2=0$

Solve each equation below and select the choice that contains *all* of the solutions.

23.
(58)
$x^4-9x^2+18=0$

A. $0,\ 3,\ -3$ B. $\sqrt{\dfrac{9+3\sqrt7}{2}},\ -\sqrt{\dfrac{9+3\sqrt7}{2}}$

C. $\sqrt6,\ -\sqrt6,\ \sqrt3,\ -\sqrt3$ D. $\sqrt2,\ -\sqrt2,\ 3,\ -3$

E. $\sqrt{-9+3\sqrt7},\ -\sqrt{-9+3\sqrt7}$

24.
(49)
$x^2=-19$

A. $-19+i,\ -19+(-i)$ B. $19i,\ -19i$ C. $\sqrt{19},\ -\sqrt{19}$

D. $\sqrt{19}i,\ -\sqrt{19}i$ E. $\sqrt{19}+\sqrt{i},\ \sqrt{19}+(-\sqrt{i})$

Translate the word problem below into an equation; then solve.

25. Hank and Aaron are 875 miles apart and headed straight toward each other. If Hank is
(15) traveling at 65 mph and Aaron is traveling at 60 mph, how many hours will it be before
the two meet?

Chapter 10 Test

Tell whether each sentence below is True or False.

1.
(63) A relationship between changing quantities can be shown with a table, an equation, or a picture (graph).

2.
(65) The graph of a linear equation (a first-degree equation with two variables) is a circle.

Calculate the value of each expression below.

3.
(22) $20 - [-2(5-1)^2 + 9]$

4.
(22) $\dfrac{4(1+2)^2}{-6+3}$

Select the factored form of each expression below.

5.
(27) $6x^2 - 10x$

    A. $2x(4x-8)$ B. $2x(3x-5)$ C. $6x(x-4)$

    D. $2x(3x-8)$ E. $10x(4x-1)$

6.
(41) $5x^2 - 11x + 2$

    A. $(5x+2)(x+1)$ B. $(5x-11)(x+2)$ C. $(5x-2)(x-1)$

    D. $(5x-1)(x-2)$ E. $(5x+1)(x+2)$

Select the simplified form of each expression below.

7.
(24) $(\dfrac{3}{4}z)(-8z^3)^2$

    A. $12z^7$ B. $48z^6$ C. $48z^7$

    D. $-7\dfrac{1}{4}z^6$ E. $-48z^7$

8.
(28) $\dfrac{x^2+2x-15}{4x} \cdot \dfrac{2x^4}{x^3+5x^2}$

    A. $\dfrac{x^2-3}{4}$ B. $\dfrac{x^2-3x}{2}$ C. $\dfrac{x^3+x^2+2x-15}{x^3+5x^2+2}$

    D. $\dfrac{x-3}{2x}$ E. $\dfrac{x^2-3x}{4}$

9.
(60)
$$\frac{x^3 + 4x^2 - 2x - 5}{x + 1}$$

    A. $x^2 + 3x - 5$ B. $x^2 + 4x - 2$ C. $x^2 + 5x + 3$

    D. $x^2 + 4x - 4$ E. $x^2 + 6x - 5$

Solve each equation below. Be sure to list only valid solutions. If an equation has no valid solutions just write "No solution."

10. $\dfrac{x}{2} - 5 = 3x + 4$ **11.** $x^3 - 7x^2 = -12x$ **12.** $\sqrt{x+5} - 5 = x$
(14)   (57)   (46)

Complete the table for the two-variable equation below.

13. $y = -2x + 6$
(63)

x	-2	-1	0	1	2	3
y	10	8	6	4		

Select the graph of the two-variable equation below.

14. $y = 3x - 2$
(66)

A.
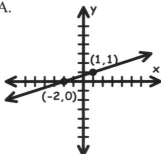

B.
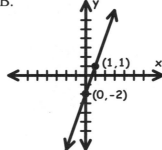

C.
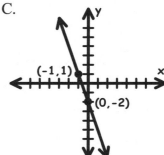

D.
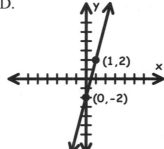

E.
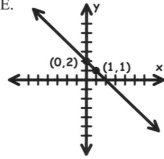

Answer each question below.

15. In the equation $y = 5x - 8$, find the value of y when $x = -4$.
(63)

16. In the equation $y = -9x$, find the value of y when $x = \dfrac{1}{3}$.
(63)

For each problem below, select the choice that represents the two-variable equation after it has been solved for y in terms of x.

17. $2y = 6x + 8$
(64)

    A. $x = \dfrac{y-4}{3}$ B. $y = 3x + 8$ C. $y = 12x + 16$

    D. $y = 3x + 4$ E. $y = 6x + 6$

18. $3x - y = 5$
(64)

    A. $y = 3x - 5$ B. $y = -3x + 5$ C. $y = 3x + 5$

    D. $y = 15x$ E. $x = \dfrac{y+5}{3}$

Find the rate of change for each two-variable equation below.

19. $y = -\dfrac{3}{2}x + 1$ **20.** $y - 4x = -7$ **21.** $y - x = 0$
(68)   (68)   (68)

Find the slope of the line below.

22.
(67)

(2,0)

(0,-3)

Select the equation for each line described below.

23. The line crossing the point $(2, 5)$ and with slope $= 4$.
(69)

    A. $y + 5 = 4(x + 2)$ B. $y + 2 = 4(x + 5)$ C. $y - 2 = 4(x - 5)$

    D. $y = 4x + 3$ E. $y - 5 = 4(x - 2)$

24. The line crossing the point $(0, 3)$ and with slope $= -\dfrac{1}{5}$.
(69)

    A. $y = -\dfrac{1}{5}x + 3$ B. $y = 3x + \dfrac{1}{5}$ C. $y = -\dfrac{1}{5}x - 3$

    D. $y = -\dfrac{1}{5}(x - 3)$ E. $y = -\dfrac{1}{5}(x + 3)$

Translate the word problem below into an equation; then solve.

25. It takes Ron 4 seconds to stack a shingle and Ben 3 seconds to do the same. How many
(9)   seconds will it take the two of them together to stack 91 shingles?

Chapter 11 Test

Tell whether each sentence below is True or False.

1. An equation for an ellipse with its center at the origin looks like $\frac{x^2}{a^2} + \frac{y^2}{b^2} = 1$, with a and
(79)
b representing the horizontal and vertical distances from the center to the edges.

2. An equation for a hyperbola with its center at the origin and opening left and right looks
(81)
like $\frac{x^2}{a^2} - \frac{y^2}{b^2} = 1$, with the points $(a, 0)$ and $(-a, 0)$ representing the vertices.

Answer each question below.

3. Tell whether the lines for $y - \frac{3}{5}x = 0$ and $y = -\frac{5}{3}x + 2$ are parallel or perpendicular.
(71)

4. Tell whether the line for $x = 7$ is horizontal or vertical.
(72)

5. Which of the following equations represents a parabola that opens downward and has a
(75) vertex at the origin?

A. $y = -\frac{1}{8}x^2$ B. $y = x^2 - 2x + 1$ C. $y = 5x^2$

D. $y = -3x^2 + 11x$ E. $y = -2x^2 + 4x + 3$

6. Which of the following equations represents a parabola that opens upward and has a
(75) vertex that is *not* at the origin?

A. $y = -\frac{1}{8}x^2$ B. $y = x^2 - 2x + 1$ C. $y = 5x^2$

D. $y = -3x^2 + 11x$ E. $y = -2x^2 + 4x + 3$

7. Tell the vertex of the parabola for the equation $y - 1 = 2(x - 3)^2$, and tell whether the
(75) parabola opens up or down.

8. Tell the center and radius of the circle for the equation $(x + 4)^2 + (y - 7)^2 = 25$.
(77)

91

Select the simplified form of each expression below.

9.
(23)
$6x^4 + (-10x^4) + 2x^4$

    A. $2x^4$ B. $6x^4$ C. $2x^{12}$

    D. $-120x^4$ E. $-2x^4$

10.
(26)
$(3y^{-5})^{-3}$

    A. $\dfrac{1}{9y^8}$ B. $-27y^8$ C. $\dfrac{y^{15}}{27}$

    D. $\dfrac{1}{27y^{15}}$ E. $\dfrac{-9}{y^8}$

11.
(27)
$\dfrac{x^2 - 3x - 10}{2x^2 + x - 6}$

    A. $\dfrac{x-5}{x+2}$ B. $\dfrac{x-5}{2x+3}$ C. $\dfrac{x+2}{2x-3}$

    D. $\dfrac{x-5}{2x-3}$ E. $\dfrac{x+5}{2x-3}$

Solve each equation below. Be sure to list only valid solutions. If an equation has no valid solutions just write "No solution."

12.
(21)
$\dfrac{1}{x-1} = \dfrac{2}{3} + \dfrac{2}{x-1}$

13.
(14)
$\dfrac{3x}{2} - 3 = 2x$

14.
(47)
$\sqrt{9x - 28} = \sqrt{5x}$

Select the graph of each two-variable equation below.

15.
(66)
$y = \dfrac{1}{2}x - 4$

    A.   B.   C.

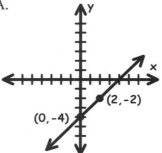
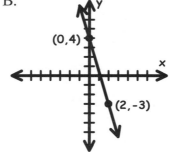
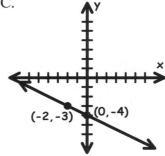

92

D.

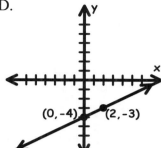

E.

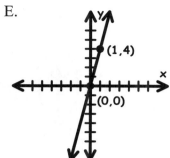

16. $y = -2x^2$
(75)

A.

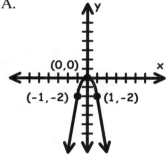

B.

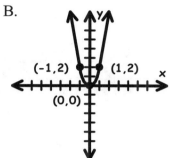

C.

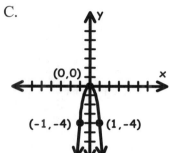

D.

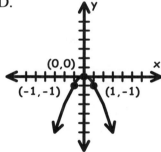

E.

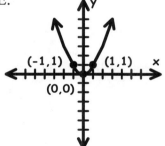

17. $\dfrac{x^2}{2^2} + \dfrac{y^2}{4^2} = 1$
(79)

A.

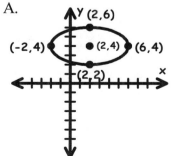

B.

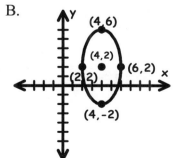

C.

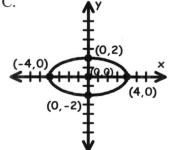

D.

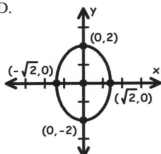

(0,2)

$(-\sqrt{2},0)$

x

$(\sqrt{2},0)$

(0,-2)

E.

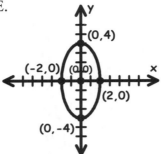

(0,4)

(-2,0) (0,0)

x

(2,0)

(0,-4)

18.
(81) $\dfrac{x^2}{5^2} - \dfrac{y^2}{3^2} = 1$

A.

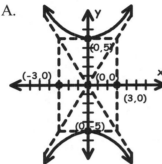

(0,5)

(-3,0) (0,0) x

(3,0)

(0,-5)

B.

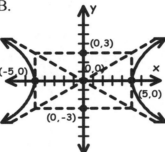

(0,3)

(-5,0) (0,0) x

(5,0)

(0,-3)

C.

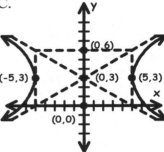

(0,6)

(-5,3) (0,3) (5,3)

x

(0,0)

D.

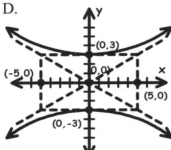

(0,3)

(-5,0) (0,0) x

(5,0)

(0,-3)

E.

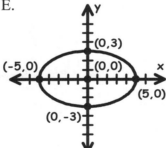

(0,3)

(-5,0) (0,0) x

(5,0)

(0,-3)

For each problem below, select the choice that represents the two-variable equation after it has been solved for *y* in terms of *x*.

19.
(64) $4y + 3x = 0$

A. $y = -\dfrac{4x}{3}$

B. $y = -\dfrac{3x}{4}$

C. $y = -12x$

D. $x = -\dfrac{4y}{3}$

E. $y = -7x$

94

20. $2y + x = 12$
(64)

    A. $y = \dfrac{-x+12}{2}$
           B. $x = -2y + 12$
           C. $y = \dfrac{-x}{2} + 12$

    D. $y = \dfrac{x-12}{2}$
           E. $y = -2x + 24$

Find the slope and *y*-intercept of the graph of each linear equation below.

21. $y - \dfrac{1}{2}x = -5$
(68)
          22. $x - 3y = 0$
(68)

Select the equation for each line described below.

23. The line crossing the point $(0, -9)$ and with slope $= 4$.
(69)

    A. $y = -36x$
           B. $y = 4x + (-9)$
           C. $y = -9x + 4$

    D. $y = 4x + 9$
           E. $y = -9x + (-4)$

24. The line crossing the points $(2, -8)$ and $(-1, -2)$.
(69)

    A. $y + 1 = -2(x + 2)$
           B. $y - 2 = 3(x - 1)$
           C. $y + 8 = -2(x - 2)$

    D. $y + 8 = -6(x - 2)$
           E. $y - 8 = -2(x + 2)$

Translate the word problem below into an equation; then solve.

25. The ratio of diners to snackers at the food court was 4 to 7. If there were 148 diners, how
(20) many snackers were there?

Chapter 12 Test

Tell whether each sentence below is True or False.

1. Three–variable equations can be graphed on a coordinate plane and their graphs are all
(85) either parabolas or circles.

2. Two of the most common standard forms are $(x+a)^2$, which equals $x^2 + 2ax + a^2$, and
(89) $(x-a)^2$, which equals $x^2 - 2ax + a^2$.

Answer each question below.

3. Find the distance between the points $(-2, -5)$ and $(3, 2)$ on the coordinate plane.
(82)

4. Tell whether the line for $y = -9$ is horizontal or vertical.
(72)

5. Tell the center and vertices of the hyperbola for the equation $\dfrac{x^2}{4^2} - \dfrac{y^2}{2^2} = 1$, and tell
(81) whether the hyperbola opens left and right or up and down.

Select the factored form of each expression below.

6. $7a^3bc^2 + 14a^2b^3c$
(88)

    A. $7a^3bc^2(1 + 2ab^2c)$ B. $14a^2bc(2ac + b)$ C. $7a^2bc(ac + 7b)$

    D. $7a^2bc(ac + 2b^2)$ E. $7a^3bc(c + 2ab)$

7. $x^2 - 2xy + y^2$
(89)

    A. $(x+y)(y-1)$ B. $(x-y)^2$ C. $(x+y)^2$

    D. $(x+y)(x-y)$ E. $(x-y)(y+1)$

8. $4s^2 - 25t^2$
(90)

    A. $(2s-5t)(2s-5t)$ B. $(2s+12.5t)(2s-12.5t)$ C. $(2s+5t)(2s+5t)$

    D. $(4s+25t)(4s-25t)$ E. $(2s+5t)(2s-5t)$

9. $ah + ak + bh + bk$
(88)

    A. $(h+k)(a+b)$ B. $(a+k)(h+b)$ C. $(a+h)(b+k)$

    D. $(a+1)(h+bk)$ E. $ab(h+k)$

Select the simplified form of each expression below.

10.
(86) $11xy^2z^3 + (-7xy^2z^3)$

    A. $4xy^2z^3$ B. $-4xy^4z^9$ C. $4x^2y^4z^6$

    D. $4xy^4z^9$ E. $-77xy^4z^9$

11.
(86) $(-3f^3g^4h^2)^2$

    A. $9f^9g^{16}h^4$ B. $-6f^6g^8h^4$ C. $9f^5g^6h^4$

    D. $-f^5g^6h^4$ E. $9f^6g^8h^4$

12.
(87) $2s^3t^2(5st - s^3t)$

    A. $-10s^7t^4$ B. $10s^3t^2 - 2s^9t^2$ C. $7s^4t^3 + s^6t^2$

    D. $10s^4t^3 - 2s^6t^3$ E. $10s^4t^3 - s^3t$

13.
(91) $\dfrac{x^2 - 2xy + y^2}{bx + cb} \cdot \dfrac{x^2 + cx}{x^2 - y^2}$

    A. $\dfrac{x-y}{bx+by}$ B. $\dfrac{x^2-xy}{b}$ C. $\dfrac{x}{b}$

    D. $\dfrac{x^2-y}{bx+y}$ E. $\dfrac{x^2-xy}{bx+by}$

14.
(91) $\dfrac{\dfrac{a}{b^2} \cdot \dfrac{b}{2a^2}}{\dfrac{3ab}{b^3} \cdot \dfrac{b^2}{2a^2}}$

    A. $\dfrac{1}{3b}$ B. $\dfrac{a}{3b^2}$ C. $\dfrac{b}{3}$

    D. $\dfrac{3}{4a^2b}$ E. $-\dfrac{1}{3b}$

15.
(93) $\dfrac{2x^3 + x^2y - 2xy^2 - y^3}{x - y}$

    A. $2x^2 - xy^2 + y^2$ B. $2x^2 + 3xy + y^2$ C. $2x^2 - xy + y^2$

    D. $2x^2 + 7xy + y^2$ E. $2x^2 + x - 2y + y^2$

Solve each equation below.

16. $-5(x+2)+3x=12$ **17.** $x^2-8x+7=0$
(10)   (40)

Solve the equation below and select the choice that contains *all* of the solutions.

18. $(x+6)^2=-13$
(55)

     A. $-3+13i,\ -3+(-13i)$ B. $-6+\sqrt{13}i,\ -6+(-\sqrt{13}i)$ C. $-19,\ -7$

     D. $+6\sqrt{13}i,\ -6\sqrt{13}i$ E. $+\sqrt{13}-6i,\ -\sqrt{13}-6i$

Answer each question below.

19. In the equation $y=ax^2+bx+c$, find the value of y when $a=3$, $b=-4$, $c=1$, and
(83) $x=-2$.

20. Which choice below represents the equation $p=\dfrac{x+q}{y+q}$ after it has been solved for q?
(84)

     A. $q=\dfrac{y-px}{p-1}$ B. $q=\dfrac{x}{py}$ C. $q=\dfrac{x+py}{p+1}$

     D. $q=\dfrac{x-py}{p-1}$ E. $q=\dfrac{p-x}{y+q}$

Select the graph of the two-variable equation below.

21. $y=0x-3$
(72)

A. 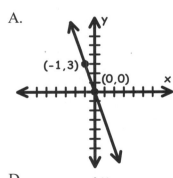   B. 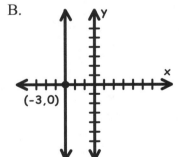   C.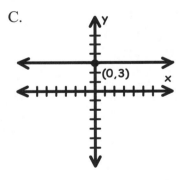

D. 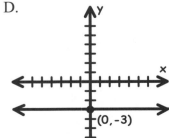   E.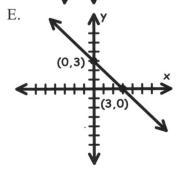

22. $x^2 + y^2 = 9$
(77)

A.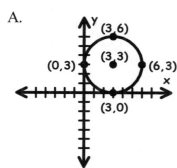

B.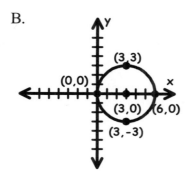

C.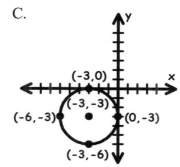

D.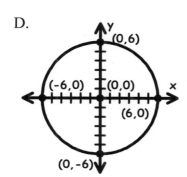

E.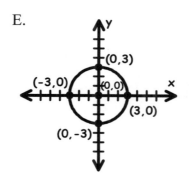

Select the equation for each line below.

23. line A
(69)

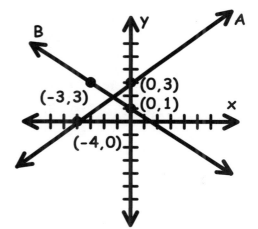

A. $y = \frac{1}{4}x + 3$

B. $y = \frac{1}{2}(x - 3)$

C. $y = \frac{3}{4}x + 3$

D. $y = \frac{3}{4}x - 3$

E. $y = \frac{3}{4}(x - 3)$

24. line B
(69)

A. $y = -\frac{2}{3}x + 1$

B. $y = -\frac{1}{2}x - 4$

C. $y = \frac{2}{3}x + 1$

D. $y - 0 = -\frac{2}{3}(x - 1)$

E. $y = -\frac{1}{3}x + 1$

99

Translate the word problem below into an equation; then solve.

25.
(10) The rectangular vegetable garden is 6 feet longer than 2 times its width. If the perimeter is 48 feet, what is the garden's width? Remember, the perimeter of a rectangle is the sum of all its sides.

Chapter 13 Test

Tell whether each sentence below is True or False.

1.
(94) A group of equations that represent a single problem is called a "system" of equations.

2.
(94) No system can ever have two pairs of solutions.

Answer each question below.

3.
(71) Tell whether the lines for $y - 3x = -5$ and $y = 3x$ are parallel or perpendicular.

4.
(79) Tell the center and vertices of the ellipse for the equation $\dfrac{(x-1)^2}{7^2} + \dfrac{(y-1)^2}{3^2} = 1$.

Select the factored form of each expression below.

5.
(88) $10x^2 y - 5x^3 y^2$

    A. $5x^3 y(2x - y)$ B. $10x^2 y(1 - 2xy)$ C. $5x^2 y(2 - xy)$

    D. $5x^2 y^2(2 - x)$ E. $5x^2 y(5 - xy)$

6.
(89) $a^2 + 2ab + b^2$

    A. $(a + b)(a + b)$ B. $(a - b)(a - b)$ C. $(a + b)(a - b)$

    D. $(b + 1)(a + b)$ E. $(a + b)(a + 1)$

Select the simplified form of each expression below.

7.
(89) $(c - v)^2$

    A. $2c - 2v$ B. $c^2 - 2cv + v^2$ C. $c^2 + v^2$

    D. $c^2 + 2cv + v^2$ E. $c^2 - v^2$

8.
(86) $(-2r^3 s^5 t^2)^4$

    A. $-8r^7 s^9 t^6$ B. $8r^{81} s^{625} t^{16}$ C. $\dfrac{1}{16r^{12} s^{20} t^8}$

    D. $-16r^{12} s^{20} t^8$ E. $16r^{12} s^{20} t^8$

9.
(92)
$$\frac{a}{ab+b^2} - \frac{b}{a^2+ab}$$

A. $\dfrac{a+b}{ab}$ B. $\dfrac{a^2-b^2}{ab}$ C. $\dfrac{a-b}{ab}$

D. 0 E. $\dfrac{1}{ab}$

10.
(87)
$(x+y)(x^2+2xy+y^2)$

A. $x^3+2xy^2+y^3$ B. $x^2+x+2xy+y+y^2$ C. $x^3+2x^2y+2xy^2+y^3$

D. $x^3+3x^2y+3xy^2+y^3$ E. $x^3+x^2y+4xy^2+y^3$

Tell whether each pair of expressions below is equivalent.

11.
(87)
$y^2-3by+2b^2$ and $(y-2b)(y-b)$

12.
(90)
$9s^2t^4-25u^2v^4$ and $(3st^2+5uv^2)(3st^2-5uv^2)$

Solve each equation below.

13.
(21)
$\dfrac{1}{x}+\dfrac{7}{5x}=\dfrac{x+2}{x}$

14.
(40)
$x^2+11x=0$

Answer each question below.

15.
(83)
In the equation $B=\dfrac{1}{3}dt^2$, find the value of B when $d=-9$ and $t=4$.

16.
(84)
Which choice below represents the equation $cdg-eg=ab$ after it has been solved for g?

A. $g=\dfrac{ab}{cd-e}$ B. $g=abcd-abe$ C. $g=\dfrac{cd-ab}{e}$

D. $g=\dfrac{ab}{cde}$ E. $g=\dfrac{cd-e}{ab}$

Select the graph of each two-variable equation below.

17.
(66) $y = -\dfrac{2}{5}x + 3$

A.
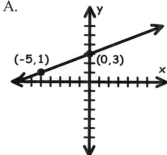

B.
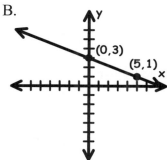

C.
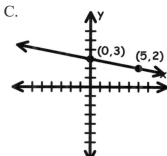

D.
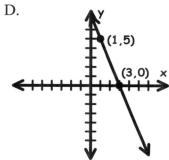

E.
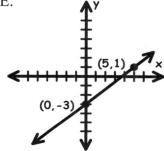

18.
(75) $y = x^2 - 4x + 9$

A.
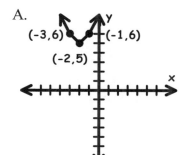

B.
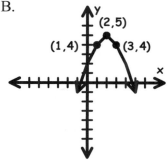

C.
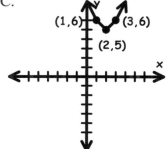

D.
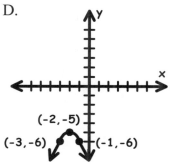

E.
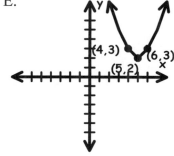

Solve each system of equations below.

19.
(94)
$$\begin{cases} 3x + 2y = -8 \\ -3x + 4y = 20 \end{cases}$$

20.
(94)
$$\begin{cases} x + 5y = -2 \\ 3x + 5y = -16 \end{cases}$$

21.
(95)
$$\begin{cases} 2x + 3y = 22 \\ 3x - 4y = -18 \end{cases}$$

22.
(96)
$$\begin{cases} 3x - y = 8 \\ y = 2x \end{cases}$$

23.
(99)
$$\begin{cases} y = 3x \\ y = x^2 + 8x + 6 \end{cases}$$

24.
(101)
$$\begin{cases} 3x - y + 2z = 15 \\ x + y + z = 4 \\ 2x - 2y + 3z = 21 \end{cases}$$

Translate the word problem below into a system of equations; then solve.

25.
(96)
Tickets to the museum exhibit cost $5.50 for adults and $3 for children. If 110 people attended and the museum sold $487.50 worth of tickets

a) How many adults attended?
b) How many children attended?

Chapter 14 Test

Tell whether each sentence below is True or False.

1.
(104) When multiplying or dividing both sides of an inequality by a negative number, the inequality symbol must be flipped.

2.
(105) In a compound inequality, the word "and" means the solutions must solve both inequalities, and the word "or" means the solutions must solve either one of the inequalities.

Select the simplified form of each expression below.

3.
(86) $(3x^2 y^4)(9x^3 y^3)(4xy^2)$

    A. $108x^5 y^9$ B. $16x^6 y^{24}$ C. $108x^6 y^9$

    D. $108x^6 y^{24}$ E. $16x^6 y^9$

4.
(93) $\dfrac{2x^3 - 6x^2 y + 5xy^2 - y^3}{x - y}$

    A. $2x^2 + 3xy + y^2$ B. $2x^2 - 2x^2 y - y^2$ C. $2x^2 - 7xy + y^2$

    D. $2x^2 - xy + y^2$ E. $2x^2 - 4xy + y^2$

Tell whether each pair of expressions below is equivalent.

5. $9a^2 - 25b^2$ and $(3a - 5b)^2$ **6.** $7x^2 + 17x - 12$ and $(7x - 4)(x + 3)$
(90)   (41)

Solve the equation below.

7.
(21) $\dfrac{x}{x - 3} - \dfrac{3}{10} = \dfrac{1}{2x - 6}$

Solve the equation below and select the choice that contains *all* of the solutions.

8.
(55) $(x - 5)^2 = -17$

    A. $+5 + \sqrt{17}i,\ -5 + \sqrt{17}i$ B. $+\sqrt{17} + 5i,\ -\sqrt{17} + 5i$

    C. $+5\sqrt{17}i,\ -5\sqrt{17}i$ D. $-5 + \sqrt{17}i,\ -5 + (-\sqrt{17}i)$

    E. $+5 + \sqrt{17}i,\ +5 + (-\sqrt{17}i)$

Answer each question below.

9. In the equation $z = \dfrac{x^3 + y^3}{2x}$, find the value of z when $x = -4$ and $y = 2$.
(83)

10. Which choice below represents the equation $a = \dfrac{j+b}{j-c}$ after it has been solved for j?
(84)

    A. $j = \dfrac{ab+c}{1-a}$ B. $j = \dfrac{ac+b}{a-1}$ C. $j = \dfrac{ac-b}{a-1}$

    D. $j = -ac + a - b - 1$ E. $j = \dfrac{b+c}{a-1}$

Select the equation for each line below.

11. line A
(69)

    A. $y = \dfrac{1}{3}x + (-2)$ B. $y = 3x + 3$

    C. $y = \dfrac{2}{3}x + 2$ D. $y = \dfrac{2}{3}x + (-2)$

    E. $y = \dfrac{2}{3}(x - 2)$

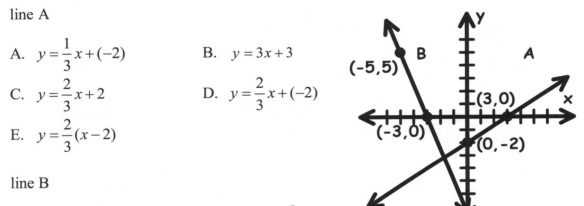

12. line B
(69)

    A. $y - 5 = -\dfrac{5}{2}(x+5)$ B. $y - 5 = -\dfrac{3}{2}(x+5)$

    C. $y + 5 = -\dfrac{5}{2}(x-5)$ D. $y + 3 = -\dfrac{1}{3}(x-0)$

    E. $y + 3 = -\dfrac{5}{2}(x-0)$

Solve each system of equations below.

13. $\begin{cases} y = \dfrac{1}{2}x \\ 2x - 3y = 5 \end{cases}$
(96)

14. $\begin{cases} x^2 + y^2 = 13 \\ y - x^2 = -7 \end{cases}$
(100)

15. $\begin{cases} x - 5y + 2z = -15 \\ 2x + 2y - z = 11 \\ x + 3y + 2z = 9 \end{cases}$
(101)

Select the correct compound inequality and its graph for each statement below.

16.
(105)

A quantity x that is greater than -5 and less than 3.

A. $x < -5$ or $x > 3$

B. $-5 \leq x \leq 3$

C. $x < 3$

D. $-5 < x < 3$

E. $x \leq -5$ or $x \geq 3$

17.
(105)

A quantity x that is less than or equal to -2 or greater than or equal to 4.

A. $-2 \leq x \leq 4$

B. $x \leq -2$ or $x \geq 4$

C. $x < -2$ or $x > 4$

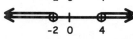

D. $x \geq 4$

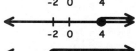

E. $x \geq -2$

Solve each inequality below and select your answer from the choices.

18.
(104)

$-3x + 7 \geq 22$

A. $x \leq -5$ B. $x \leq 12$ C. $x \geq -5$

D. $x \geq -7$ E. $x \geq 12$

19.
(104)

$-7(x+1) \leq -2(x-5)$

A. $x \geq \dfrac{17}{5}$ B. $x \geq -\dfrac{6}{5}$ C. $x \geq -\dfrac{3}{5}$

D. $x \leq -\dfrac{17}{9}$ E. $x \geq -\dfrac{17}{5}$

20.
(106)

$3y^2 > 108$

A. $y > 6$ B. $y < -105$ or $y > 105$ C. $y < -6$ or $y > 6$

D. $y < -6$ E. $-6 < y < 6$

21. $x^2 - 3x - 40 < 0$
(107)

    A. $x < -8$ or $x > 5$ B. $x < -5$ or $x > 8$ C. $-10 < x < 4$

    D. $-5 < x < 8$ E. $-8 < x < 5$

22. $4x - 8 \leq -16$ or $4x - 8 \geq 4$
(105)

    A. $-2 \leq x \leq 3$ B. $x \leq -2$ or $x \geq 3$ C. $x \leq -6$ or $x \geq 3$

    D. $x \leq -3$ or $x \geq 2$ E. $-6 \leq x \leq 3$

Select the graph of each system of inequalities below.

23. $\begin{cases} y < -2x - 1 \\ y < 2x + 3 \end{cases}$
(110)

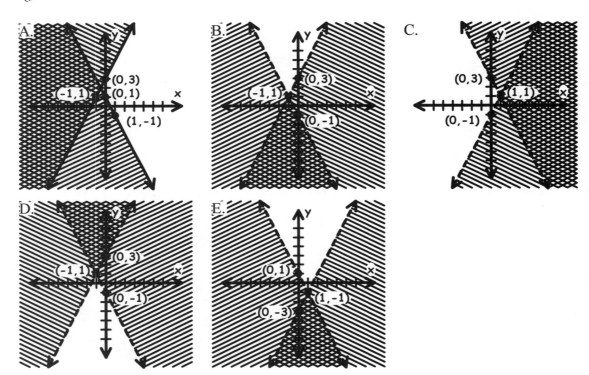

24.
(110)
$$\begin{cases} y \geq 3x - 2 \\ y \leq x \end{cases}$$

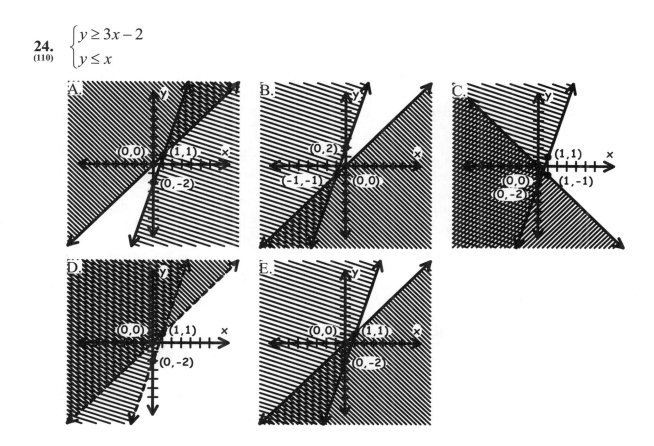

Translate the word problem below into an inequality; then solve.

25. Mrs. Dundee wants to sell the rights to her new Cajun cookbook and she has two offers.
(104) The first publisher has offered to pay $80,000 up front and a $3 royalty for every book sold. The second publisher has offered to pay $30,000 up front and $5 for every book sold. Over what range of sales will Mrs. Dundee make more from the second publisher than from the first?

Chapter 15 Test

Tell whether each sentence below is True or False.

1.
(112) One way to understand absolute value is as the difference between two numbers.

2.
(112) Another way to understand absolute value is as the positive of whatever quantity is inside the absolute-value bars.

Calculate each absolute value below.

3.
(112) $\left|-9\right|$

4.
(112) $\left|15-10\right|$

Select the factored form of each expression below.

5.
(90) $4a^2b^2 - 9c^2d^2$

    A. $(4ab + 9cd)(4ab - 9cd)$ B. $(2ab + 4.5cd)(2ab - 4.5cd)$ C. $(2ab + 3cd)^2$

    D. $(2ab - 3cd)^2$ E. $(2ab + 3cd)(2ab - 3cd)$

6.
(89) $x^2 + 2ax + a^2$

    A. $(x + a)^2$ B. $(x + a)(x - a)$ C. $(x + a)(x + 1)$

    D. $(x - a)^2$ E. $(x + a)(a + 1)$

Select the simplified form of each expression below.

7.
(86) $\dfrac{4}{5}x^3y^4 - \dfrac{1}{5}x^3y^4$

    A. $\dfrac{3}{5}x^6y^8$ B. $-\dfrac{4}{25}x^9y^{16}$ C. $\dfrac{3}{5}x^3y^4$

    D. $-\dfrac{4}{25}x^3y^4$ E. $\dfrac{3}{5}$

8.
(12) $2[3x - (4 + 5x)] + 11x$

    A. $-x$ B. $7x - 4$ C. $27x - 8$

    D. $7x - 8$ E. $15x - 8$

9.
(18)
$$\dfrac{\dfrac{y-4}{3(y-1)}}{\dfrac{2y-8}{15}}$$

A. $\dfrac{5}{2y-2}$ B. $\dfrac{1}{5y-5}$ C. $\dfrac{10}{y-1}$

D. $\dfrac{6}{y-1}$ E. $\dfrac{2y^2-16y+32}{45y-45}$

Solve each equation below.

10. $2(x+1)+5x=-17$ **11.** $\dfrac{1}{x}+\dfrac{2}{5x}=\dfrac{2}{10-5x}$
(10) (21)

Answer each question below.

12. In the equation $Q=0.5an^3$, find the value of Q when $a=5.2$ and $n=1.7$. Round your
(83) answer to two decimal places (hundredths).

13. Which choice below represents the equation $y=\dfrac{z^3}{ax}$ after it has been solved for x?
(84)

A. $x=\dfrac{ay}{z^3}$ B. $x=\dfrac{z^3}{y}-a$ C. $x=\dfrac{az^3}{y}$

D. $x=\dfrac{1}{z^3ay}$ E. $x=\dfrac{z^3}{ay}$

Solve each system of equations below.

14. $\begin{cases}2x-4y=-26\\3x-5y=-31\end{cases}$ **15.** $\begin{cases}y=x^2-1\\y=3x+3\end{cases}$
(95) (99)

Solve each inequality below and select your answer from the choices.

16. $2x-7>8(x-3)$
(104)

A. $x>\dfrac{17}{10}$ B. $x<\dfrac{17}{10}$ C. $x<\dfrac{31}{6}$

D. $x<\dfrac{17}{6}$ E. $x<-\dfrac{2}{3}$

17.
(107)

$x^2 + 9x \geq -18$

A. $x \leq -1$ or $x \geq 18$

B. $x \leq -6$ or $x \geq -3$

C. $-9 \leq x \leq -2$

D. $x \leq -9$ or $x \geq -2$

E. $-6 \leq x \leq -3$

Select the graph of each system of inequalities below.

18.
(110)

$\begin{cases} x + y > 2 \\ y - 2x < -4 \end{cases}$

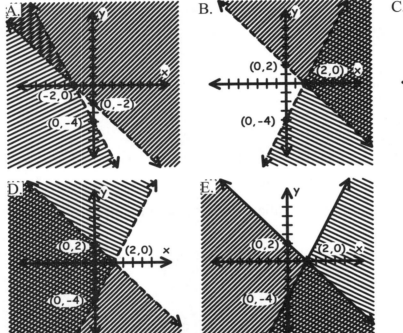

19.
(110)

$\begin{cases} y \geq 3x - 4 \\ 2x + y \leq 1 \end{cases}$

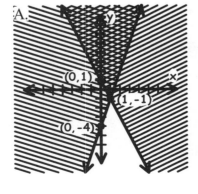
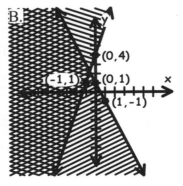

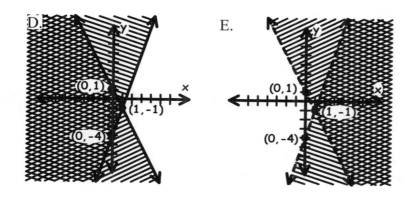

Solve each absolute-value equation below. If an equation has no solutions just write "No solutions."

20.
(114) $|x - 9| = 23$

21.
(114) $|3x + 4| = 11$

22.
(113) $\left|\dfrac{1}{2}x - 13\right| = -7$

Solve each absolute-value inequality below and select your answer from the choices.

23.
(115) $|3x - 3| \leq 18$

 A. $x \leq 7$ B. $-7 \leq x \leq 7$ C. $x \leq -5$ or $x \geq 7$

 D. $-5 \leq x \leq 7$ E. $x \leq -7$ or $x \geq 7$

24.
(115) $\left|\dfrac{1}{4}x + 1\right| > 2$

 A. $x < -12$ or $x > 4$ B. $-3\dfrac{1}{4} < x < \dfrac{3}{4}$ C. $x < -4$ or $x > 12$

 D. $-12 < x < 4$ E. $x > 4$

Translate the word problem below into a system of equations; then solve.

25.
(95) Harrison paid \$36.50 for 5 cans of yellow tennis balls and 3 cans of white ones. Beverly paid \$50.25 for 7 cans of yellow tennis balls and 4 cans of white ones. If they both paid the same prices,

 a) How much did each can of yellow tennis balls cost?
 b) How much did each can of white tennis balls cost?

Chapter 16 Test

Tell whether each sentence below is True or False.

1.
(116)   A function is a relationship (between variables) where starting with a value for x, there is only one matching value for y.

2.
(118)   To shift the graph of a function vertically, you add a positive or negative number to the function and make it the last operation done to x.

Find each logarithm below without using a calculator.

3. $\log_{13} 13$
(125)

4. $\log_{19} 1$
(125)

5. $\log_8 8^5$
(125)

Select the simplified form of each expression below.

6. $(-7x^3 y^5)(5x^2 y^2)(2xy)$
(86)

    A. $-70x^6 y^{10}$ B. $x^6 y^8$ C. $-35x^5 y^7$

    D. $70x^9 y^{25}$ E. $-70x^6 y^8$

7. $\dfrac{2x}{2x-8} - \dfrac{x}{x-4}$
(28)

    A. 0 B. $\dfrac{2x}{x-4}$ C. $\dfrac{1}{2x-8}$

    D. $\dfrac{4x}{x-4}$ E. $-\dfrac{x^2}{x^2-8x+16}$

Solve each equation below.

8. $-4.2x - (x-3) = 44.6$
(10)

9. $\dfrac{2}{7-x} = \dfrac{1}{x}$
(21)

Solve the equation below and select the choice that contains *all* of the solutions.

10. $2x^2 + 18 = 0$
(49)

    A. $3i$, $-3i$ B. $3\sqrt{i}$, $-3\sqrt{i}$ C. $3\sqrt{2}i$, $-3\sqrt{2}i$

    D. $3-i$, $-3-i$ E. 3, -3

Solve each exponential equation below using a calculator. Round each answer to four decimal places.

11. $10^x = 199$
(124)

12. $6^{9x-4} = 44$
(125)

Select the domain and range of each function below.

13. $y = -9x^2$
(116)

    A. Domain: All real numbers; Range: All real numbers
    B. Domain: All real numbers less than or equal to 0; Range: All real numbers
    C. Domain: All real numbers except 0; Range: All real numbers except 0
    D. Domain: All real numbers; Range: All real numbers less than or equal to 0
    E. Domain: All real numbers; Range: All real numbers less than or equal to -9

14. $y = \dfrac{5}{2x}$
(116)

    A. Domain: All real numbers; Range: All real numbers
    B. Domain: All real numbers except 0; Range: All real numbers
    C. Domain: All real numbers except 0; Range: All real numbers except 0
    D. Domain: All real numbers; Range: All real numbers except 0
    E. Domain: All real numbers; Range: All real numbers greater than or equal to $\dfrac{5}{2}$

Select the function for each graph described below.

15. The graph of $y = 7x^2 - 10$ shifted 5 places to the right.
(118)

    A. $y = 7x^2 - 15$ B. $y = 7x^2 - 5$ C. $y = 7(x-5)^2 - 5$

    D. $y = 7(x-5)^2 - 10$ E. $y = 7(x+5)^2 - 10$

16. The graph of $y = x^4$ shifted up 4 places and 7 places to the left.
(118)

    A. $y = (x-4)^4 - 7$ B. $y = (x+4)^4 + 7$ C. $y = (x+7)^4 - 4$

    D. $y = (x+7)^4 + 4$ E. $y = (x-7)^4 + 4$

Match each graph below to one of the equation choices.

17.
(118)

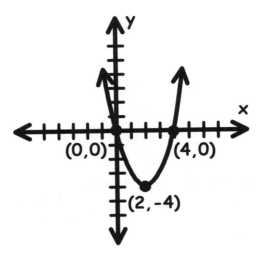

A. $y = (x-4)^2 + 2$ B. $y = (x-2)^2 - 4$ C. $y = -2x^2 - 4$

D. $y = (x+4)^2 - 2$ E. $y = (x-2)^2 + 4$

18.
(118)

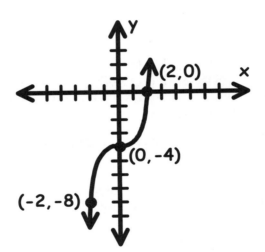

A. $y = \dfrac{1}{2}x^3 + 2$ B. $y = \dfrac{1}{2}x^3 + 4$ C. $y = \dfrac{1}{2}(x+4)^3$

D. $y = \dfrac{1}{2}(x-4)^3$ E. $y = \dfrac{1}{2}x^3 - 4$

Select the correct function in each problem below.

19. If $U(x) = -4x^2$ and $V(x) = x - 3$, find $U(x) \cdot V(x)$.
(120)

A. $-4x^2 + x - 3$ B. $-4x^3 + 12x^2$ C. $-4x^2 - 12$

D. $-4x^2 + 24x - 36$ E. $-4x^3 - 12x^2$

116

20. If $r(x) = x^2 + 2$ and $x(t) = 3t - 4$, find $r(x(t))$.
(120)

    A. $3tx^2 + 6t - 4x^2 - 8$ B. $9t^2 - 24t + 16$ C. $9t^2 - 24t + 18$

    D. $9t^2 + 18$ E. $x^2 + 3t - 2$

Graph each equation below with a graphing calculator and select the choice that matches your graph.

21. $y = -x^3 + 4x^2 - 5$
(121)

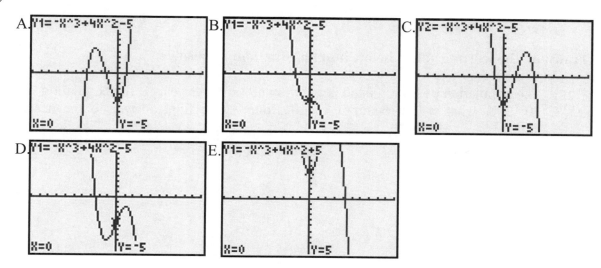

22. $y = -x^5 + 3x^4 + 3x^3 - 9x^2 - 2x$
(121)

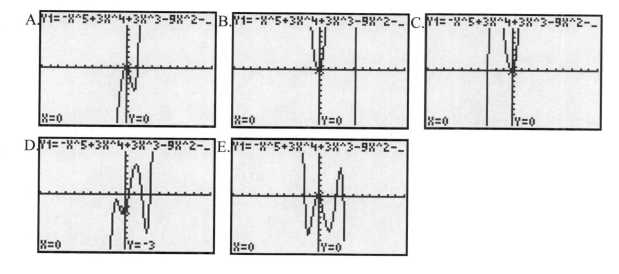

Answer each question below.

23. Find the distance between the points $(0,\ 1)$ and $(4,\ 4)$ on the coordinate plane.
(82)

24. Which choice below represents the equation $cm + d = m$ after it has been solved for m?
(84)

  A. $m = \dfrac{d}{1-c}$ B. $m = \dfrac{d}{2c}$ C. $m = -\dfrac{d}{c}$

  D. $m = c + d$ E. $m = \dfrac{d}{c+1}$

Translate the word problem below into an equation; then solve.

25. The population of Euler Island is growing at 3.6% per year. If the population is currently
(122) 105,000, what will it be in 9 years? Round your final answer to the nearest whole number.

Chapter 17 Test

Tell whether each sentence below is True or False.

1.
(126) The mode of a group of data is the number that appears the most frequently.

2.
(129) If when one variable goes up the other variable tends to go up (roughly), the variables are negatively correlated.

Answer each question below.

3.
(126) The table below shows the ACT math scores of all of the members of the City Center homeschool chess club. Find the mean, median, and mode of the data.

ACT Math Scores

32	36	26	26	25	26	21	35
26	27	33	27	34	29	25	32

4.
(126) A local bank offered one $20,000 scholarship, two $10,000 scholarships, and twenty $1,000 scholarships. Select the best measure of central tendency for the data.

A. Mean   B. Median   C. Mode

5.
(128) A set of data with 1,200 numbers is normally distributed with a mean of 27 and a standard deviation of 4. How many numbers in the data would you expect to be between 23 and 31?

6.
(128) A set of data with 1,200 numbers is normally distributed with a mean of 27 and a standard deviation of 4. How many numbers in the data would you expect to be between 19 and 35?

Find the indicated value of the dependent variable for the function $f(t) = 75(1 + 0.27)^t$.
Round your answer to two decimal places (hundredths).

7. $f(6)$
(117)

8. $f(18)$
(117)

Calculate the range and standard deviation of each group of data below. Round your answers to two decimal places (hundredths).

9.
(127) 40, 65, 33, 46, 55, 50, 61

10.
(127) 94, 92, 88, 83, 84, 78, 90

Select whether each scatter plot below shows a positive correlation, a negative correlation, or no correlation between the variables.

11.
(129)

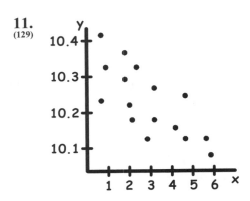

A. Positive correlation
B. Negative correlation
C. No correlation

12.
(129)

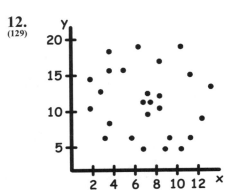

A. No correlation
B. Positive correlation
C. Negative correlation

Answer each question below.

13.
(130) A teacher's desk contains 3 black permanent markers, 2 red magic markers, and 5 blue magic markers. What is the probability of pulling out (without looking) a magic marker? Write your answer as a fully reduced fraction.

14.
(132) What is the probability of flipping a coin 3 times and having it land heads on the first two flips and tails on the third? Write your answer as a fully-reduced fraction.

15.
(131) Seven people are trying to get into a taxi that will only seat 3 people. How many seating arrangements are possible?

16.
(131) At the local cafeteria today, 6 side dishes are being offered: asparagus, steamed rice, fried okra, sweet potatoes, beans, and zucchini. The daily lunch special includes only 4 side dishes. How many combinations of side dishes are possible?

17.
(131) How many different 9-letter "words" can you make by arranging the letters in DEVIATION? The arrangements don't have to be actual words that are included in any dictionary.

18. Emily is purchasing a new printer for $180. She can also purchase a warranty at an
(133) additional cost of $25. With the warranty, Emily can get the printer replaced for free,
should it ever break. If there's a 6% probability that the printer will break during the time
Emily owns it, what is the expected value of the warranty? Should she purchase it?

Select the equation for each line described below.

19. The line crossing the point $(0,7)$ and with slope $= -4$.
(69)

    A. $y = 4x + 7$ B. $y + 7 = -4(x - 0)$ C. $y - 4 = 7(x - 0)$

    D. $y = 7x - 4$ E. $y = -4x + 7$

20. The line crossing the points $(-2, -3)$ and $(6, 1)$.
(69)

    A. $y - 1 = 2(x - 6)$ B. $y + 1 = \dfrac{1}{2}(x + 6)$ C. $y + 2 = 2(x + 3)$

    D. $y - 3 = \dfrac{1}{2}(x - 2)$ E. $y - 1 = \dfrac{1}{2}(x - 6)$

Solve each inequality below and select your answer from the choices.

21. $-9x + 11 \le 38$
(104)

    A. $x \le -3$ B. $x \le 18$ C. $x \ge -3$

    D. $x \ge -\dfrac{49}{9}$ E. $x \le 3$

22. $5x^2 \le -15x$
(107)

    A. $-3 \le x \le 0$ B. $x \le -3$ or $x \ge 0$ C. $0 \le x \le 3$

    D. $x \ge 3$ or $x \le 0$ E. $-15 \le x \le 5$

Answer each question below.

23. Which choice below represents the equation $t = 2u + 2v$ after it's been solved for v?
(84)

    A. $v = \dfrac{t - u}{2}$ B. $v = t - 2u$ C. $v = \dfrac{t}{u}$

    D. $v = \dfrac{t - 2u}{2}$ E. $v = \dfrac{t + 2u}{2}$

24. Which choice below represents the equation $z = \dfrac{k+l}{w}$ after it's been solved for w?
(84)

    A. $w = k + l - z$ B. $w = zk + zl$ C. $w = k + l + z$

    D. $w = \dfrac{z}{k+l}$ E. $w = \dfrac{k+l}{z}$

Translate the word problem below into an equation; then solve.

25. Cordell and Bonnie are 675 miles apart and headed straight toward each other. If Cordell
(15) is traveling at 75 mph and Bonnie is traveling at 60 mph, how many hours will it be
before the two cars are side-by-side?

Chapter 18 Test

Tell whether each sentence below is True or False.

1.
(134)
A geometric sequence is a sequence where each term comes from adding the same number to the previous term.

2.
(135)
To divide two complex numbers, you multiply the top and bottom (of the fraction) by the conjugate of the denominator.

3.
(136)
A matrix is a rectangular array of numbers (or possibly variables) in rows and columns.

Calculate the value of each expression below and select your answer from the choices. Make sure to fully simplify your answers.

4.
(52)
$(-3i^4)^3$

    A. $27i$ B. -27 C. -9

    D. $-9i^7$ E. $-27i$

5.
(52)
$(2+7i)(-9+i)$

    A. $-11+(-61i)$ B. $-18+(-54i)$ C. $-7+8i$

    D. $-25+(-61i)$ E. $-18+7i^2$

6.
(135)
$\dfrac{7+4i}{4+5i}$

    A. $\dfrac{48}{41}+\left(-\dfrac{19}{41}i\right)$ B. $\dfrac{8+51i}{-9+40i}$ C. $\dfrac{8}{41}+\left(-\dfrac{19}{41}i\right)$

    D. $\dfrac{65}{8+19i}$ E. $-\dfrac{48}{9}+\dfrac{19}{9}i$

7.
(135)
$\dfrac{4+(-3i)}{1+(-4i)}$

    A. $-\dfrac{8}{17}+\dfrac{13}{17}i$ B. $-\dfrac{16}{15}+\left(-\dfrac{13}{15}i\right)$ C. $\dfrac{16}{17}+\dfrac{13}{17}i$

    D. $\dfrac{25}{16+(-13i)}$ E. $\dfrac{-8+(-19i)}{-15+(-8i)}$

If $A = \begin{bmatrix} -4 & 5 & 6 \\ -8 & -1 & 3 \end{bmatrix}$, $B = \begin{bmatrix} 17 & 0 & 27 \\ -2 & 12 & 9 \end{bmatrix}$, and $c = 3$, select the answer to each operation below.

8. $A + B$
(136)

A. $\begin{bmatrix} 21 & 5 & 33 \\ 10 & 13 & 12 \end{bmatrix}$ B. $\begin{bmatrix} -21 & 5 & -21 \\ -6 & -13 & -6 \end{bmatrix}$ C. $\begin{bmatrix} 13 & 5 & 33 \\ -10 & 11 & 12 \end{bmatrix}$

D. $\begin{bmatrix} -12 & 15 & 18 \\ -24 & -3 & 9 \end{bmatrix}$ E. $\begin{bmatrix} 13 & 5 & 33 \\ 10 & -3 & -6 \end{bmatrix}$

9. $B - A$
(136)

A. $\begin{bmatrix} -21 & 5 & -21 \\ -6 & -13 & -6 \end{bmatrix}$ B. $\begin{bmatrix} -12 & 15 & 18 \\ -24 & -3 & 9 \end{bmatrix}$ C. $\begin{bmatrix} 21 & -5 & 21 \\ 6 & 13 & 6 \end{bmatrix}$

D. $\begin{bmatrix} 13 & 5 & 33 \\ -10 & 11 & 12 \end{bmatrix}$ E. $\begin{bmatrix} 13 & -5 & 21 \\ -10 & 11 & 6 \end{bmatrix}$

10. cA
(136)

A. $\begin{bmatrix} 51 & 0 & 81 \\ -6 & 36 & 27 \end{bmatrix}$ B. $\begin{bmatrix} -68 & 0 & 162 \\ 16 & -12 & 27 \end{bmatrix}$ C. $\begin{bmatrix} -1 & 8 & 9 \\ -5 & 2 & 6 \end{bmatrix}$

D. $\begin{bmatrix} -64 & 125 & 216 \\ -512 & -3 & 27 \end{bmatrix}$ E. $\begin{bmatrix} -12 & 15 & 18 \\ -24 & -3 & 9 \end{bmatrix}$

Find the next three terms of each sequence below.

11. 64, 48, 32…
(134)

12. 7, 21, 63...
(134)

Answer each question below.

13. Find the 81st term for the sequence 12, 18, 24, 30...
(134)

14. Find the 11th term for the sequence 8, 24, 72, 216...
(134)

15. Select the direct formula for the sequence 11, 22, 33, 44, ...
(134)

    A. $a_n = 11 + (n-1)11$ B. $a_n = 11 + (n-1)2$ C. $a_n = 11 \cdot 11^{n-1}$

    D. $a_n = 11 \cdot 2^{n-1}$ E. $a_n = 11 + (n-1)22$

16. Select the direct formula for the sequence 13, 91, 637, 4,459, ...
(134)

    A. $a_n = 7 \cdot 13^{n-1}$ B. $a_n = 13 + (n-1)6$ C. $a_n = 13 \cdot 6^{n-1}$

    D. $a_n = 13 \cdot 7^{n-1}$ E. $a_n = 13 + (n-1)7$

Solve each equation below.

17. $2[3(x+4)] - 15 = 4x$ **18.** $\dfrac{3}{4x} + \dfrac{2}{x-1} = \dfrac{5}{2x}$ **19.** $y^2 - 3y = 40$
(14)   (21)   (40)

Answer each question below.

20. In the equation $f = \dfrac{a^2 - b^2}{c}$, find the value of f when $a = -5$, $b = -2$, and $c = 7$.
(83)

21. Which choice below represents the equation $d = 16t^2$ after it has been solved for t?
(84)

    A. $t = \pm 4\sqrt{d}$ B. $t = \pm\sqrt{d-16}$ C. $t = \dfrac{d}{16}$

    D. $t = \dfrac{d}{32}$ E. $t = \dfrac{\pm\sqrt{d}}{4}$

22. Which choice below represents the equation $ax - b = x$ after it has been solved for x?
(84)

    A. $x = a - b$ B. $x = \dfrac{b}{a-1}$ C. $x = \dfrac{b}{a}$

    D. $x = \dfrac{b}{1-a}$ E. $x = b - a$

Solve each system of equations below using determinants.

23. $\begin{cases} -4x + y = -5 \\ 2x - 5y = 7 \end{cases}$ **24.** $\begin{cases} 4x - 7y = -4 \\ -5x + 8y = 2 \end{cases}$
(137)   (137)

Translate the word problem below into an equation; then solve.

25. Bradford put some of his $25,000 in savings in a stock mutual fund and the rest in a bond
(11) mutual fund. If Bradford earned 9% on the money he put in the stock mutual fund and
6% on the money he put in the bond mutual fund, and his combined earnings were
$1,893, how much did he invest in the stock mutual fund?

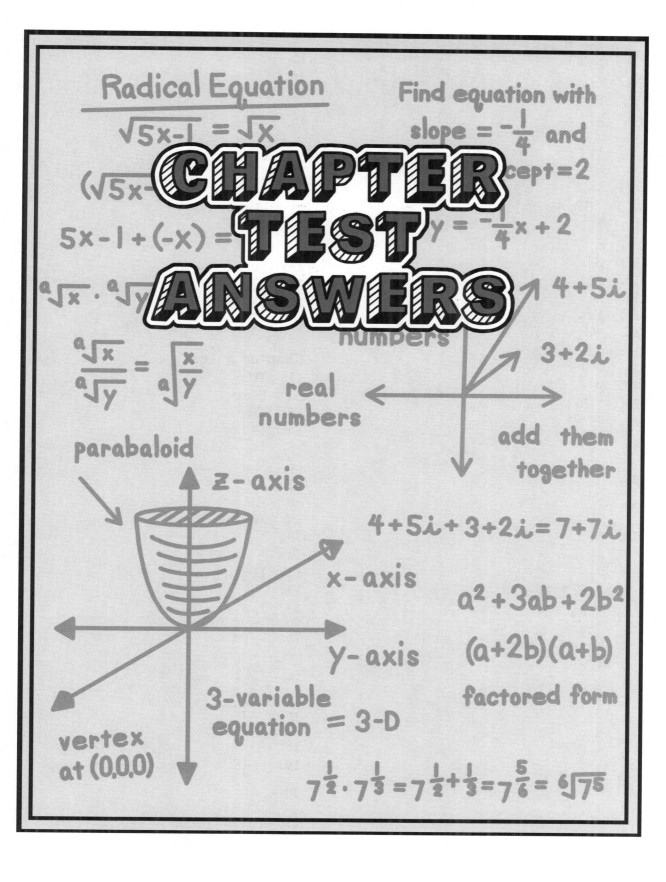

Radical Equation

$$\sqrt{5x-1} = \sqrt{x}$$

$$(\sqrt{5x-} $$

$$5x-1+(-x)=$$

$$\sqrt[a]{x} \cdot \sqrt[a]{y}$$

$$\frac{\sqrt[a]{x}}{\sqrt[a]{y}} = \sqrt[a]{\frac{x}{y}}$$

parabaloid

z-axis

x-axis

y-axis

vertex
at (0,0,0)

3-variable
equation = 3-D

Find equation with
slope $= -\frac{1}{4}$ and
cept $= 2$

$$y = -\frac{1}{4}x + 2$$

real
numbers

numbers

$4+5i$

$3+2i$

add them
together

$$4+5i+3+2i=7+7i$$

$$a^2+3ab+2b^2$$

$$(a+2b)(a+b)$$

factored form

$$7^{\frac{1}{2}} \cdot 7^{\frac{1}{3}} = 7^{\frac{1}{2}+\frac{1}{3}} = 7^{\frac{5}{6}} = \sqrt[6]{7^5}$$

CHAPTER TEST ANSWERS

Chapter 1 Test

1. True
2. False
3. True
4. B
5. C
6. 25
7. 30
8. -44
9. -37
10. 7
11. E
12. B
13. A
14. D
15. Yes
16. No
17. 22
18. 7
19. 9
20. -102
21. 29
22. $\dfrac{4}{3}$
23. 16.2
24. $\dfrac{11}{6}$
25. $3

Chapter 2 Test

1. True
2. True
3. B
4. C
5. 2
6. 6
7. 33
8. Yes
9. Yes
10. E
11. B
12. C
13. A
14. D
15. B
16. 7
17. 16
18. $-\dfrac{12}{5}$
19. 2
20. $-\dfrac{2}{3}$
21. Identity
22. $\dfrac{6}{5}$
23. False equation
24. 1
25. $35,000

Chapter 3 Test

1. True
2. False
3. True
4. 14
5. 115
6. 3
7. E
8. E
9. A
10. C
11. E
12. D
13. No
14. No
15. $\dfrac{5}{9}$
16. $\dfrac{55}{8}$
17. $-\dfrac{2}{3}$
18. 3
19. -48
20. $\dfrac{4}{13}$
21. False equation

22. $\dfrac{5}{7}$

23. $-\dfrac{10}{3}$

24. 19 cans

Chapter 4 Test
1. True
2. True
3. True
4. 38
5. -4
6. -147
7. 5.4×10^9
8. 2.7×10^{-8}
9. 1.792×10^{12}
10. 1.76×10^{-4}
11. Yes
12. Yes
13. B
14. A
15. D
16. B
17. E
18. D
19. 2
20. 4
21. $-\dfrac{19}{5}$
22. $\dfrac{7}{5}$
23. 4
24. $\dfrac{3}{4}$
25. 195 gallons

Chapter 5 Test
1. True
2. True
3. 14,800,000
4. 0.00076
5. Irrational
6. Rational
7. 3.61
8. 4.12
9. $5^{\frac{1}{2}}$
10. $3^{\frac{2}{5}}$
11. D
12. E
13. A
14. B
15. C
16. D
17. E
18. A
19. B
20. B
21. C
22. 2
23. 23
24. -12
25. 13 hours

Chapter 6 Test
1. False
2. True
3. 1.344×10^{-3}
4. 3×10^{-8}
5. B
6. E
7. A
8. D
9. C
10. A
11. D
12. B
13. Yes
14. No
15. $\dfrac{5}{3}$
16. 4, -14
17. D
18. 0, -4

19. 7, 3
20. $\frac{5}{2}$, −1
21. E
22. A
23. D
24. 8, 40

Chapter 7 Test

1. True
2. True
3. $a = 4$, $b = 2$, $c = -1$
4. $a = 3$, $b = -5$, $c = -11$
5. B
6. $\sqrt{7}$
7. $5^{\frac{7}{12}}$
8. E
9. A
10. C
11. A
12. C
13. A
14. Yes
15. Yes
16. $-\frac{1}{10}$
17. 49
18. 1
19. 6 (3 is extraneous)
20. 16
21. A
22. −7, 5
23. D
24. 93 quarters

Chapter 8 Test

1. True
2. True
3. Real solutions
4. Complex solutions
5. E

6. A
7. D
8. C
9. A
10. E
11. B
12. C
13. A
14. A
15. E
16. B
17. C
18. D
19. $\frac{1}{2}$, 0
20. $\frac{25}{2}$
21. 5, −5
22. C
23. E
24. C
25. 30 degrees

Chapter 9 Test

1. True
2. True
3. 6.74
4. −3.05
5. Complex solutions
6. Real solutions
7. Complex solutions
8. A
9. E
10. A
11. E
12. D
13. B
14. E
15. A
16. B
17. D
18. E

19. $\dfrac{9}{13}$
20. $0, -1, -3$
21. 24
22. $2, 1, -1$
23. C
24. D
25. 7 hours

Chapter 10 Test

1. True
2. False
3. 43
4. -12
5. B
6. D
7. C
8. B
9. A
10. $-\dfrac{18}{5}$
11. $4, 3, 0$
12. $-4, -5$
13. $y = -2x + 6$

x	-2	-1	0	1	2	3
y	10	8	6	4	2	0

14. B
15. $y = -28$
16. $y = -3$
17. D
18. A
19. $-\dfrac{3}{2}$
20. 4
21. 1
22. $\dfrac{3}{2}$
23. E
24. A
25. 156 seconds

Chapter 11 Test

1. True
2. True
3. Perpendicular
4. Vertical
5. A
6. B
7. vertex $(3, 1)$; opens up
8. center $(-4, 7)$; radius 5
9. E
10. C
11. D
12. $-\dfrac{1}{2}$
13. -6
14. 7
15. D
16. A
17. E
18. B
19. B
20. A
21. Slope $\dfrac{1}{2}$; y-intercept $(0, -5)$
22. Slope $\dfrac{1}{3}$; y-intercept $(0, 0)$
23. B
24. C
25. 259 snackers

Chapter 12 Test

1. False
2. True
3. $\sqrt{74}$
4. Horizontal
5. Center $(0, 0)$; vertices $(4, 0)$, $(-4, 0)$; opens left/right
6. D
7. B
8. E
9. A
10. A

11. E
12. D
13. E
14. A
15. B
16. −11
17. 7, 1
18. B
19. $y = 21$
20. D
21. D
22. E
23. C
24. A
25   6 feet

Chapter 13 Test

1. True
2. False
3. Parallel
4. Center $(1, 1)$; vertices $(8, 1)$ $(-6, 1)$
5. C
6. A
7. B
8. E
9. C
10. D
11. Yes
12. Yes
13. $\dfrac{2}{5}$
14. 0, −11
15. $B = -48$
16. A
17. B
18. C
19. $x = -4$, $y = 2$
20. $x = -7$, $y = 1$
21. $x = 2$, $y = 6$
22. $x = 8$, $y = 16$
23. $x = -2$, $y = -6$ and $x = -3$, $y = -9$

24. $x = 1$, $y = -2$, $z = 5$
25. a) 63 adults
     b) 47 children

Chapter 14 Test

1. True
2. True
3. C
4. E
5. No
6. Yes
7. $-\dfrac{4}{7}$
8. E
9. $z = 7$
10. B
11. D
12. A
13. $x = 10$, $y = 5$
14. $x = 2$, $y = -3$ and $x = -2$, $y = -3$
     and $x = 3$, $y = 2$ and $x = -3$, $y = 2$
15. $x = 2$, $y = 3$, $z = -1$
16. D
17. B
18. A
19. E
20. C
21. D
22. B
23. B
24. E
25. More than 25,000 books.

Chapter 15 Test

1. True
2. True
3. 9
4. 5
5. E
6. A
7. C
8. D

9. A
10. $-\dfrac{19}{7}$
11. $\dfrac{14}{9}$
12. $Q = 12.77$
13. E
14. $x = 3$, $y = 8$
15. $x = 4$, $y = 15$ and $x = -1$, $y = 0$
16. D
17. B
18. B
19. D
20. $32, -14$
21. $\dfrac{7}{3}, -5$
22. No solutions
23. D
24. A
25. a) $4.75 for each can of yellow
    b) $4.25 for each can of white

Chapter 16 Test
1. True
2. True
3. 1
4. 0
5. 5
6. E
7. A
8. -8
9. $\dfrac{7}{3}$
10. A
11. 2.2989
12. 0.6791
13. D
14. C
15. D
16. D
17. B
18. E
19. B

20. C
21. C
22. E
23. 5
24. A
25. 144,353

Chapter 17 Test
1. True
2. False
3. Mean = 28.75; Median = 27; Mode = 26
4. C
5. 816
6. 1,140
7. 314.69
8. 5,540.24
9. Range = 32, Standard Deviation = 10.53
10. Range = 16, Standard Deviation = 5.21
11. B
12. A
13. $\dfrac{7}{10}$
14. $\dfrac{1}{8}$
15. 210
16. 15
17. 181,440
18. $10.80; No
19. E
20. E
21. C
22. A
23. D
24. E
25. 5 hours

Chapter 18 Test
1. False
2. True
3. True
4. B

5. D
6. A
7. C
8. C
9. C
10. E
11. 16, 0, −16
12. 189; 567; 1,701
13. 492
14. 472,392
15. A
16. D
17. $-\dfrac{9}{2}$
18. −7
19. 8, −5
20. $f = 3$
21. E
22. B
23. $x = 1$, $y = -1$
24. $x = 6$, $y = 4$
25. $13,100